MATH
DICTIONARY
&
SURVIVAL GUIDE
VOLUME ONE

Paulette Clarke & Barbara Gajdos

Project Manager: Carla Belanger
Desktop Publishing: Mandy Christiansen

We gratefully acknowledge the support of the
Alberta Foundation for the Arts for our publishing program.

ROGUEMEDIA
www.roguemedia.ca

ISBN: 978-1-897372-03-6

11 10 09 08 07 06 • 9 8 7 6 5 4 3 2

W9-CTS-857

A

Acronym

A word or abbreviation that is formed by taking the first letter of each word to help in memory recall.

Example: EMS is the acronym for Emergency Medical Services.

Acute angle

An angle that measures between 0° and 90°.

Example:

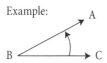

$\angle ABC$ is an acute angle.

Acute triangle

A triangle that has three acute angles.

Example:

$\triangle ABC$ is an acute triangle.

Addend

A number added to one or more numbers.

Example: "2 + 3 + 4" has three addends (2, 3 and 4)

Addition

A mathematical operation in which two or more numbers are combined to give a total (sum).

Example: $2 + 3 = 5$

Additive inverse

A number that has the same numeric value, but opposite sign.

Example: The additive inverse of +3 is -3.
          The additive inverse of -10 is +10.

Additive inverse property

The sum of a number and its additive inverse equals 0.

Example: $(+4) + (-4) = 0$
          $(-7) + (+7) = 0$

Adjacent
Lying immediately next to each other.

Example:

The triangles are adjacent to each other.

Adjacent angles
Angles that share a vertex and a side.

Example:

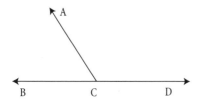

$\measuredangle ACB$ is adjacent to $\measuredangle ACD$.

Adjacent sides
Sides that have a common vertex.

Example:

$\overline{AB}$ is adjacent to $\overline{BC}$ because they share vertex B.

Algebra
A type of mathematics that uses symbols to represent unknown values.

Example: $x + 4 = 9$

$2xy$

Algebraic equation
A mathematical equation containing one or more variables.

Example: "$n + 5 = 8$" is an algebraic equation.

"$2x + 3y = 10$" is an algebraic equation.

Algebraic expression
A mathematical expression containing one or more variables.

Example: "2x – 5" is an algebraic expression.

Algebraic terms

Parts of an algebraic expression separated by operations of addition and/or subtraction.

Example: The algebraic expression "$2x + 4$" has two terms: $2x$ and 4.

The algebraic expression "$3x + 4y - 5$" has three terms: $3x$, $4y$ and -5.

Algebra tiles

Rectangular shapes used to illustrate positive (shaded) and negative (unshaded) numbers and variables.

Example:

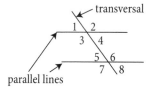

Alternate angles

Pairs of angles formed on the outside or inside of two parallel lines, but on opposite sides of the transversal.

Example: $\angle 3$ and $\angle 6$, $\angle 4$ and $\angle 5$, $\angle 1$ and $\angle 8$, $\angle 2$ and $\angle 7$ are all alternate angles.

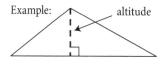

Altitude

A line segment drawn from the vertex of an object perpendicular to the opposite side.

Example:

And

A decimal point in a number.

Example: four and seven-tenths
"and" means there is a decimal point in the number
four and seven-tenths = 4.7

Another word for addition.

Example: four and seven-tenths
"and" means four added to seven-tenths
four and seven-tenths = $4 + \dfrac{7}{10}$

Angle
An intersection of two rays at a common point called the vertex.

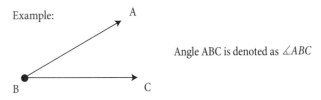

Angle ABC is denoted as $\angle ABC$

Angle bisector
A line segment that cuts an angle into two symmetrical halves.

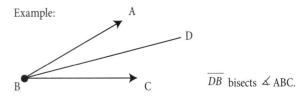

$\overline{DB}$ bisects $\angle$ ABC.

Angle of depression
The angle formed between a horizontal line of sight and a point below the line of sight.

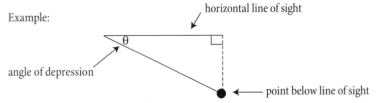

Angle of elevation
The angle formed between a horizontal line of sight and a point above the line of sight.

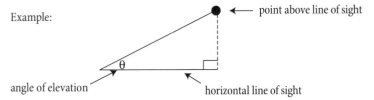

Angle of rotation
The amount of degrees an object is turned.

Example:

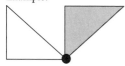

The white triangle was rotated clockwise; the shaded triangle is the result.
The angle of rotation was 90°.

Area
A two dimensional measurement showing the amount of surface an object covers.

Example:

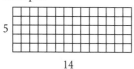

The area of the rectangle is 70 square units.

ASA
A congruency theorem which states if two angles and an included side of one triangle are equal in measurements to two corresponding angles and an included side of another triangle, the triangles are congruent.

Example:

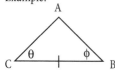 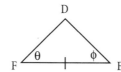

△ ABC ≅ △ DEF by ASA

Ascending
Objects or numbers arranged in sequential order from smallest to largest.

Example: 2, 6, 10, 13, 15, 19, 20, 25
The set of numbers is in ascending order.

Associative property
A property for adding or multiplying groups of numbers that states "the order in which numbers are added or multiplied does not change the sum or product".

Example: (3 + 2) + 5   =   3 + (2 + 5)
5 + 5   =   3 + 7
10   =   10

(3 × 2) × 5   =   3 × (2 × 5)
6 × 5   =   3 × 10
30   =   30

Average
A single number that is used to represent or summarize a set of numbers (see mean, median, mode).

> Example: {3, 7, 17, 33}
>
> The sum of the set (60) ÷ the number of items in the set (4) = 15.
>
> The average is 15.

Axis
A line of reference on a graph or object. Plural is **axes**.

Example:

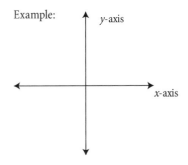

Axis of symmetry
A line that cuts a two-dimensional object into two symmetrical halves.

Example:

A rectangle has two lines of symmetry.

B

Balance
Equal in value; both sides of an equation having the same numeric value.

Example:

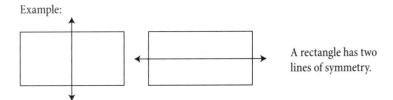

This equation is "balanced" if ⬛ = ☐☐☐☐☐☐☐

Bar graph

A visual representation of data in which the height of horizontal or vertical bars show the quantity of items in a particular set.

Example: The bar graph below shows the use of game systems among teens.

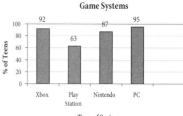

Base

of a Polygon: The lowest part of a polygon; the bottom edge of a polygon.

Example:

base

of a 3-D shape:
Example:

Bases of a right prism: the two unique shapes bounded by rectangular sides. For the prism below, the bases are the two hexagons.
Note: "base" is not synonymous with "bottom".

Base of a pyramid: the unique shape bounded by triangular sides, as in the pentagonal pyramid at the right.

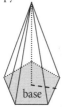

of a Power: The factor in repeated multiplication; the number that is raised to an exponent.

Example: In the example 5^4, "5" is the base. 5 is the factor multiplied by itself 4 times $(5 \times 5 \times 5 \times 5)$.

Base plan
Two dimensional drawing showing the side, top and front view of a three dimensional object.

Example:

Side View   Front View

Top View

This is the base plan for the following three dimensional shape.

BEDMAS
An acronym to remember the order of operations used in questions with two or more operations.

Example:

B	Brackets
E	Exponents
D	Division
M	Multiplication
A	Addition
S	Subtraction

Bias
To be influenced by or prejudiced by something external.

Example: Sally wanted to take a survey to determine whether hockey was a violent sport. She stood outside the hockey arena before the big game and asked every third person.

This shows "bias" because people at a hockey game most likely don't think hockey is too violent or they would not attend the game. Her results of the survey would be biased.

Binomial
An algebraic expression or polynomial with two terms.

Example: "$3x + 3$" and "$3x^2y + x$" are binomials.

Bisect

To divide a line segment or an angle into two equal parts.

Example:

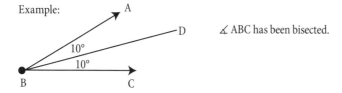

∡ ABC has been bisected.

Box and whisker plot

Visual representation of a set of numbers showing the median, extreme values and how spread out the data is.

Example:

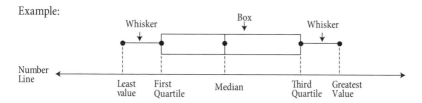

Brackets

A pair of symbols, ( ), in which numeric values are inserted.

Example: In doing a check of an algebraic equation, the variable is replaced with the solution using brackets.

$$x + 4 \quad = 5$$
$$(1) + 4 \quad = 5$$
$$5 \qquad = 5$$

In order of operations, operations inside brackets are preformed first.

$$(3 + 5) \times 4$$
$$8 \times 4$$
$$32$$

A pair of symbols, { }, to denote a set or collection of items with similar characteristics.

Example: {1, 2, 3, 4, 5, 6 ...} is the set of all natural numbers.

Broken line graph

A visual representation of a data set using line segments connected end to end; often used to show trends in data.

Example: The school concession is keeping track of their profits. The graph below represents their profit over the past five months.

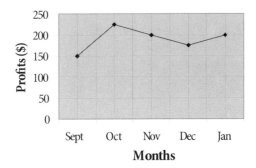

School Concession Profits

C

Calculate

To figure out the numeric value or answer to a question in mathematics.

Example: Calculate $(3 + 5) \times 4$.
$(3 + 5) \times 4$
8×4
32 ◄─────── this is $(3 + 5) \times 4$ "calculated".

Capacity

Amount of fluid or solid a container can hold.

Example:

The milk jug, when filled to its capacity, can hold 2L of milk.

Cartesian coordinate system

Four sections or quadrants formed by the intersection of two axes: the horizontal (x-axis) and the vertical (y-axis). The Cartesian coordinate system is used to graph relations.

Example:

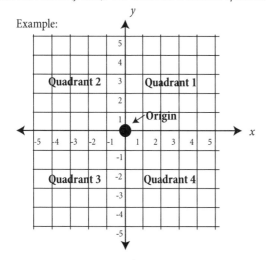

The above illustrates the Cartesian coordinate system.

Chance

The likelihood or probability an event will occur.

Example: When you flip a coin, there is a 50% chance it will land on tails.

Check

To substitute the value of the variable in the original equation with the solution and use order of operations to see if a true statement is reached.

Example: $5y$ =   35
$\quad\quad\quad\quad$ $5(7)$ =   35
$\quad\quad\quad\quad$ 35   =   35 √

This verifies that $y = 7$ is the solution to the equation $5y = 35$. The above process is called a "check".

Chord

A line segment formed by connecting two points on a circle's circumference.

Example:

Circle

A closed shape with an infinite number of points equal distance from a fixed point called the centre.

Example:

Circle graph

A graph that uses sections of a circle to show how data is divided into parts.

Example:

Circumference

The distance around the outside of a circle; the perimeter of a circle.

Example:

Clockwise

Moving around a circle in the same direction the hands of clock move; right to left.

Example:

Cluster
A group of numbers close together.

Example: 0

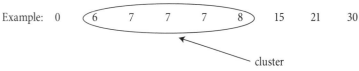

cluster

Coefficient
A number placed in front of a variable.

Example: $5y$

"5" is the coefficient

Column
Arranged vertically; in a table numbers that can be read up and down.

Example:

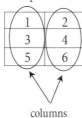

This table has two columns.

columns

Combine like terms
To add or subtract terms in which the variable and the exponent are identical by adding or subtracting the coefficient and leaving the variable alone.

Example: $y^2 - 2y^2$

$= -y^2$

Commission
The amount of money paid to a salesperson based on total amount of sales.

Example: A salesperson receiving commission of 20% on all sales would receive $200 for selling $1 000 of merchandise.

$1 000 \times 0.20 = 200

Common denominator
A common multiple of the denominators in two or more fractions.

Example: For the fractions $\frac{1}{2}, \frac{2}{5}, \frac{3}{4}$ have a common denominator of 20 because LCM $(2, 4, 5) = 20$.

Common factor

Factors shared among numbers.

Example: Factors of 18: **1, 2, 3, 6**, 9, 18

Factors of 24: **1, 2, 3**, 4, **6**, 8, 12, 24.

The common factors of 18 and 24 are 1, 2, 3, and 6.

Common multiple

Multiples shared among numbers.

Example: Multiples of 4: 4, 8, 12, 16, **20**, 24, 28, 32, 36, **40**, 44, 48, 52, 56, **60**…

Multiples of 10: 10, **20**, 30, **40**, 50, **60**…

The common multiples of 4 and 10 are 20, 40, 60… The list of common multiples is infinite.

Commutative property

A property for multiplying or adding groups of numbers that states interchanging the numbers does not change the product or the sum.

Example: $5 + 9 \quad = 9 + 5$ $\qquad 4 \times 5 \quad = 5 \times 4$

$14 \qquad = 14$ $\qquad\qquad 20 \qquad = 20$

Compare

Find similarities and/or differences between numbers or objects.

Example: Similarities: $2\frac{1}{3}$ and $\frac{5}{4}$ are both rational numbers.

Differences: $2\frac{1}{3}$ is a mixed number, $\frac{5}{4}$ is an improper fraction.

$2\frac{1}{3}$ is larger than $\frac{5}{4}$.

The above are all ways of comparing $2\frac{1}{3}$ and $\frac{5}{4}$.

Complementary angles

Two angles whose sum is 90°.

Example:

$\angle$ ABD and $\angle$ CBD are complementary angles.

Composite figure
A two dimensional shape made up of simpler geometric shapes.

Example:

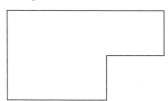

Composite number
A number that has three or more factors.

Example: Factors of 12: 1, 2, 3, 4, 6, 12
12 is a composite number.

Composite solid
A three dimensional geometric solid made up of simpler geometric solids.

Example:

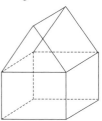

Cone
A three-dimensional solid that has a circular base and comes to a point at the top.

Example:

Congruent
Equal or exactly the same.

Example:

The squares are congruent.

Congruent triangles
Triangles are identical in shape and size.

Example:

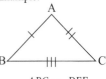

$\triangle ABC \cong \triangle DEF$

$\triangle ABC$ is congruent to $\triangle DEF$

Consecutive numbers
Numbers written in order one after the other.

Example: 11, 12, 13, 14, … are consecutive numbers.

Constant
A value that remains the same and does not change.

Example: $x + 6$
"6" is a constant.

Continuous Data
Data in which the in-between points are meaningful; histograms and line graphs are used to display continuous data.

Example: "Hours Worked" and "Amount Paid" are examples of continuous data because you can work in-between 4 and 5 hours and you can make in-between $6 and $7 dollars.

Control variable
A factor held constant to test the impact of another variable.

Example: In testing the gas consumption of various vehicles, the control variable would be driving the same distance with each vehicle. By driving the same distance, gas consumption can be fairly tested; i.e. number of litres of fuel/100 km.

Convert
To change the form in which something is presented; to write in a different way.

Example: $\dfrac{5}{4} = 1.25$
$\dfrac{5}{4}$ was converted to a decimal.

Coordinate plane

Four sections or quadrants formed by the intersection of two axes: the horizontal (*x*-axis) and the vertical (*y*-axis). The coordinate plane is used to graph relations.

Example:

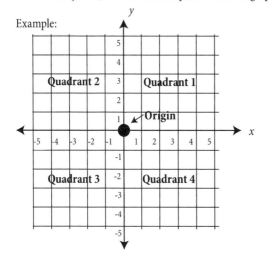

The above illustrates the Cartesian coordinate system.

Coordinates

Pairs of numbers that describe the location of a point on the coordinate plane compared to the origin.

Example: (2, -5) is the coordinate 2 units right and 5 units down from the origin.

Correlation

The relationship between two or more variables.

Example: The relationship between height and weight.

Corresponding angles

Pairs of angles formed on the outside or inside of two parallel lines on the same side of the transversal.

Example: $\angle 1$ and $\angle 5$, $\angle 2$ and $\angle 6$, $\angle 3$ and $\angle 7$, $\angle 4$ and $\angle 8$ are all corresponding angles.

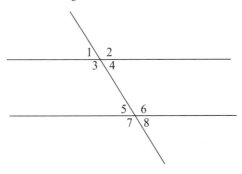

Corresponding sides

Line segments with the same relative position within a geometric shape.

Example: $\overline{FE}$ corresponds to $\overline{AB}$, $\overline{FD}$ corresponds to $\overline{AC}$, and $\overline{ED}$ corresponds to $\overline{BC}$.

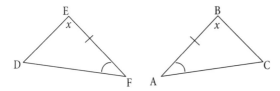

Cosine

A trigonometric ratio used in right triangles comparing the adjacent side to the hypotenuse from a given angle's perspective.

Example:

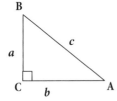

$$\text{Cos} \angle A = \frac{b}{c} \qquad \text{Cos} \angle B = \frac{a}{c}$$

Counterclockwise
Moving around a circle in the opposite direction; left to right.

Example:

Cube
A three dimensional solid made up of six congruent square faces.

Example:

Cubed
A number raised to the exponent of three.

Example: 7^3

Cubic metre
Common unit used to measure volume.

Example: m^3 is the amount of space that a cube measuring 1 m by 1 m by 1 m would occupy.

Cylinder
A three-dimensional solid made up of two congruent and parallel circular bases and a curved rectangular section connecting the two bases.

Example:

D

Data
A collection of information, usually in the form of numbers, which can be used to calculate statistics and draw conclusions from.

Example: Percentage scores of 15 students' exam marks:

| 56 | 82 | 42 | 95 | 67 | 75 | 34 | 77 | 66 |
| 71 | 74 | 68 | 80 | 82 | 45 | 90 | 95 | 67 |

Data analysis
Interpreting statistical information and drawing conclusions based on a given data set.

Example: Percentage scores of 15 students' exam marks:

56	82	42	95	67	75	34	77	66
71	74	68	80	82	45	90	95	67

Data analysis:

The mean of this set of data is 70.3, the median is 72.5, 34 and 95 are the extremes and the range is 61. There are three modes for this set of data 67 and 82 and 95. Three students failed the exam. Etc…

Decagon
A polygon with ten sides.

Example:

Decimal
A whole number and/or parts of a whole number.

Example: 123.56 is a decimal.

Decimal point
The "dot" in a decimal used to separate the whole number from the part of a whole number.

Example:

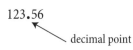

123.56

decimal point

Degree
Temperature: The measurement on a thermometer used to determine how hot or cold it is.

Example:

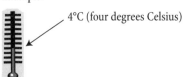

4°C (four degrees Celsius)

of an angle:
A measure of rotation between two rays that intersect in a common vertex. 1° is equal to $\frac{1}{360}$ of a complete rotation. In the example below, $\angle ABC = 73°$.

Example:

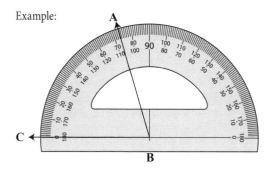

of a monomial: The sum of the exponents of all the variables.

Example: $3x^3y^4z$ has a degree of 8 $(3 + 4 + 1 = 8)$

of polynomials:
1 variable: The highest exponent among the terms.

Example: $2x^4 + 3x^5$ has a degree of 5 because 5 is the highest exponent of any one term.

2+ variables: The highest sum of the exponents among the terms.

Example: $x^4yz - 3x^3y^2 + 4$ has a degree of 6 because 6 $(4 + 1 + 1)$ is the largest sum of the exponents in any one term.

Denominator
The bottom number in a fraction; it shows the number of equal parts a whole is divided into or the total number of items in a set.

Example: $\frac{2}{5}$ "5" is the denominator.

Density
The ratio of mass to volume.

Example: Density $= \dfrac{mass}{volume}$

Dependent variable
A variable whose value relies (depends) on the value of another variable (independent variable).

Example: The distance a car can travel in an hour is dependent upon the speed at which it is traveling. The distance is the dependent variable.

Descending

Objects or numbers arranged in sequential order from largest to smallest.

Example: 25, 20, 19, 15, 13, 10, 6, 2

The set of numbers is in descending order.

Descending order (of a polynomial)

Terms of a polynomial arranged so that the exponents of one variable are arranged in order from largest to smallest.

Example: $4x - y^3 + 5x^2y$ arranged in descending powers of x:

$5x^2y + 4x - y^3$

Diagonal

A line segment that connects two non-adjacent vertices of a polygon.

Example:

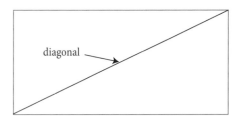

diagonal

Diameter

The distance from one side of the circle to the other through the centre; a chord that passes through the centre.

Example:

Difference

The distance between two numbers, or the result of subtracting two numbers.

Example: The difference between 18 and 4 is 14.

Digit

Any one of the ten numerals (0, 1, 2, 3, 4, 5, 6, 7, 8, 9) used to form numbers.

Example: The number 12 456 has 5 digits (1, 2, 4, 5 and 6).

Dilatation

A transformation that makes an object either larger or smaller by multiplying or dividing each side length of an object by the same amount. The dilatation is also known as a "dilation".

Example:

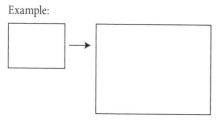

Each side of the original rectangle was made two times larger.

Dimension

The side lengths of a geometric figure.

Example:

3 cm

11 cm

The rectangle has dimensions of 11 cm by 3 cm.

Discount

The amount of money an object will be reduced in price by; the amount of money you will save.

Example: An item regularly priced at $50.00 is on sale for 10% off.

The discount or amount of money you will save is $5.00 ($50 \times 0.10$).

Discrete Data

Data in which the in-between points are not meaningful; bar graphs and scatter plots are used to display discrete data.

Example: "Number of movie tickets" and "Number of people" are examples of discrete data because you cannot buy half a ticket and you cannot have one-third a person.

Distribution

How spread out the numbers in a set of data are, or how data is placed within frequency intervals. Distribution can be illustrated using box and whisker plots or histograms.

Example:

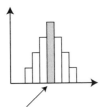 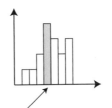 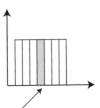

This data has an even distribution; it peaks in the middle and there is an equal amount of numbers in the intervals above and below the middle interval.

This data doesn't have an even distribution; there are more numbers above the middle interval than below. The data is skewed to the right.

This data has a uniform distribution; each interval has an equal amount of numbers in it. Every interval is equal.

Distributive property

A property that allows you to remove the brackets by multiplying each of the terms inside the brackets by the term outside of the brackets.

Example:

$2(x + 4)$
$2 \times x + 2 \times 4$
$2x + 8$

Dividend

The number to be divided into equal groups; the first number in a division sentence.

Example: $24 \div 4 = 6$

"24" is the dividend.

Divisibility tests

Rules used to determine whether one number is divisible by another number.

Example:

2: A number is divisible by 2 if the last digit is even (ends in a 0, 2, 4, 6, or 8).
Example: 14 796
- is divisible by 2 because the last digit (6) is even.

3: A number is divisible by 3 if the sum of its digits is divisible by 3.
Example: 9 273
- $9 + 2 + 7 + 3 = 21$
- 21 is divisible by 3 therefore, 9 273 is divisible by 3.

4: A number is divisible by 4 if the number formed by the last two digits is divisible by 4.
Example: 1 624
- The last two digits are 24.
- 24 is divisible by 4 therefore, 1 624 is divisible by 4.

5: A number is divisible by 5 if the last digit is a 0 or a 5.
Example: 89 235
- The last digit is 5.
- Therefore, 89 235 is divisible by 5.

6: A number is divisible by 6 if it is divisible by 2 AND by 3.
Example: 32 784

- 32 784 is divisible by 2 and 3, therefore 32 784 is divisible by 6.

7: A number is divisible by 7 if the difference of double the last digit subtracted from the rest of the number is divisible by 7.
Example: 7 035
- $703 - 2(5) = 693$
- 693 is divisible by 7 therefore, 7 035 is divisible by 7.

8: A number is divisible by 8 if the number formed by the last three digits is divisible by 8.
Example: 32 160
- The last three digits are 160.
- 160 is divisible by 8 therefore, 32 160 is divisible by 8.

9: A number is divisible by 9 if the sum of its digits is divisible by 9.
Example: 203 805
- $2 + 0 + 3 + 8 + 0 + 5 = 18$
- 18 is divisible by 9 therefore, 203 805 is divisible by 9.

10: A number is divisible by 10 if the last digit is a 0.
Example: 356 870

- 356 870 is divisible by 10 because it ends in a 0.

Divisible

A number that divides into another number with no remainder.

Example: 30 is "divisible" by 5 because $30 \div 5 = 6$ (no remainder).

Divisor
The number of groups an object is to be divided into; the second number in a division sentence.

Example: $24 \div 4 = 6$
                    "4" is the divisor.

Dodecagon
A polygon with twelve sides.

Example:

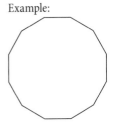

E

Edge
The line segment formed when two faces of a three dimensional shape meet.

Example:

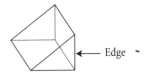
← — Edge

Element
A member of a set.

Example: -5 is an element of the Integers because it is a negative whole number.
                    $-5 \in I$

Elevation view
Two dimensional drawing showing the numbers of layers of a three dimensional object based on its top view.

Example:

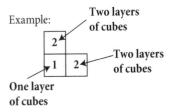
Two layers of cubes
Two layers of cubes
One layer of cubes

This is the elevation view for the following three-dimensional object:

Enlargement

A transformation in which an object is made larger. The shape is the same, but the image is larger than the original object.

Example:

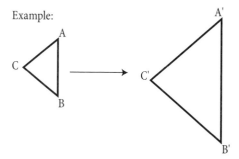

Equal

Identical and balanced or having the same value.

Example: $5 + 4 = 9$
$9 = 9$

Both sides of the equation have the same value and are therefore "equal".

Equally likely outcome

In probability, two events that have the same chance of occurring.

Example: Flipping a tail on a coin has an equally likely outcome as rolling an even number on a 6-sided dice.

Equation

A mathematical statement that contains an equal sign.

Example: $3 + 5 = 8$ is an equation.

Equilateral triangle

A triangle with three sides of equal length.

Example:

Equivalent

Having the same value.

Example: $\frac{1}{2}$ is equivalent to 50%.

Equivalent fractions

Fractions that look different but have the same value. Equivalent fractions, in lowest terms, would be identical.

Example: $\frac{1}{2}$ and $\frac{2}{4}$ are equivalent fractions.

Estimate

A reasonable guess or approximate calculation.

Example: I estimate the distance from my house to school to be 4 km.

Evaluate

To find the numeric value of a mathematical expression.

Example: $54 \div 6 + 2 \times 4 - 4$, when evaluated, is 13.

Even number

A number divisible by two.

Example: 14 is an even number ($14 \div 2 = 7$).

Even vertex

A point at which an even number of line segments or arcs meet.

Example:

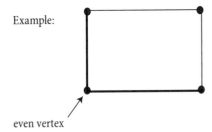

even vertex

Event

In probability, a subset of a sample space for a given experiment.

Example: Tossing a coin has a sample space of {heads, tails}. Tossing a head is an "event".

Expand

To remove the brackets and simplify.

Example: $3mn(2m + 3)$
$= 6m^2n + 9mn$

Expanded form

of numbers: To write a number as an addition sentence using all of its values.

Example: $1\,205\,302 = 1\,000\,000 + 200\,000 + 5\,000 + 300 + 2$

of powers: The number written as repeated multiplication. Also known as factored form.

Example: $7 \times 7 \times 7$

Expected value

The number of times an event should occur.

Example: If a coin is tossed 80 times, how many times would you expect it to land on tails?

Expected value = Number of trials × P(event)
Expected value = $80 \times \dfrac{1}{2}$
Expected value = 40

You would expect the coin to land on tails about 40 times.

Experimental probability

The chance or likelihood of an event occurring based on a simulation or trial.

Example: A coin was tossed 40 times and the number of heads and tails was recorded.

If the coin landed on tails 33 times, the experimental probability of tails is $\dfrac{33}{40}$.

Exponent

The number of times the base used as a factor.

Example: $7^4 = 7 \times 7 \times 7 \times 7$
"4" is the exponent.

Exponential form

A number written in the form of a power.

Example: 49 written in exponential form is 7^2.

Express

To write a number based on a set of instructions; to find an equivalent way of representing a value.

Example: Express $\dfrac{4}{10}$ in lowest terms.
This means to write $\dfrac{4}{10}$ as a fraction in lowest terms ($\dfrac{2}{5}$).

Expression

A combination of numbers and mathematical operations.

Example: "5 + 7" and "3 − 7 × 4" are expressions.

Exterior angles on the same side of the transversal

Angles formed on the outside of parallel lines, but on the same side of the transversal.

Example: ∡1 and ∡7 are exterior angles on the same side of the transversal as are ∡2 and ∡8.

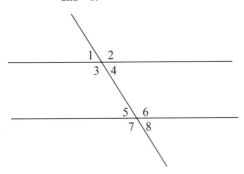

Extrapolate

To estimate values beyond the range of given values.

Example:

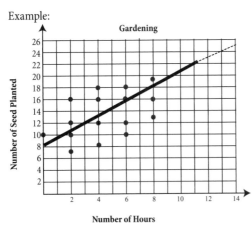

It would take about 14 hours to plant 25 seeds. This is an example of extrapolation because the estimate falls beyond the range of values.

Extremes

The largest and smallest values in a given set.

Example:

F

Face

A two dimensional side of a three dimensional shape.

Example:

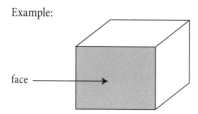

face

Factor

of numbers: Two or more numbers that multiply to any given number.

   Example: 3 and 5 are two factors of 15 (3 × 5 = 15).

of polynomials: Two or more polynomials that multiply to any given polynomial.

   Example: $2m$ and $3mn$ are two factors of $6m^2n$ ($2m \times 3mn = 6m^2n$).

to factor: Write a polynomial as a product of simpler polynomials.

   Example: $3m^2n - 6mn^2$ factored is $3mn(m - 2n)$.
              $x^2 - 4x + -5$ factored is $(x - 5)(x + 1)$.

Factor tree

A tree diagram used to find the prime factorization of a number. Starting with the number at the top, two factors are listed below it. The branch of the tree ends when a prime factor is reached. Each number that is not a prime number is further broken down until all the factors of the original number are prime numbers.

Example:

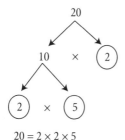

$20 = 2 \times 2 \times 5$

F

False statement
A statement that is not correct or true.

Example:

$x = 5$ in the equation $x + 4 = 6$

$x + 4 = 6$

$(5) + 4 = 6$

$9 \neq 6$

A false statement was reached $(9 \neq 6)$ therefore $x = 5$ is not the solution.

Flip
A transformation in which a figure is reflected about a line of reference called the axis of symmetry. Also known as a reflection.

Example:

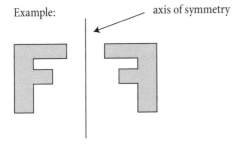

axis of symmetry

FOIL
An acronym used to remember the order of multiplying two binomials together.

Example:

First terms	$(x)(x) = x^2$
Outside terms	$(2)(x) = 2x$
Inside terms	$(2)(x) = 2x$
Last terms	$(2)(2) = 4$

F   O   I   L

$x^2 + 2x + 2x + 4$

Formula
A rule, using variables and/or constants, in the form of an equation used to calculate unknown values.

Example: $P = 2l + 2w,$

$A = l \times w,$

$D = \dfrac{S}{T}$ and

$C = \pi d$ are all formulas.

Four-colour theorem

A rule that states any map can be coloured using at most four colours so that no adjacent regions are coloured with the same colour.

Example:

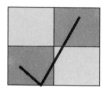

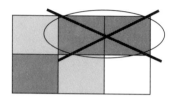

This is correct because no adjacent regions have the same colour.

This is incorrect because two of the adjacent regions have the same colour.

Fraction

A number that is not a whole number. A number that is part of a whole number or part of a set.

Example: $\frac{1}{2}$, $4\frac{2}{5}$ and $\frac{5}{4}$ are all fractions.

Frequency

The number of times something occurs.

Example: A survey among 15 people showed that 1 person liked Rap music, 5 people liked country music, 2 people liked Jazz music and 3 people liked Pop music.

Frequency table

A table used to organize data with tallies and frequencies.

Example:

Favourite Music	Tally	Frequency
Country	⊬⊬⊬	5
Rock	||||	4
Pop	|||	3
Jazz	||	2
Rap	|	1

Function

A relationship between two sets of numbers; members of one set of numbers map onto members of another set of numbers.

Example:

x	y
-2	-5
-1	-4
0	-3
1	-2
2	-1

G

Geometry

A type of mathematics that studies the shape, size and movement of one dimensional, two dimensional and three dimensional objects.

Example: Area, perimeter, surface area, volume, lines, rays, graphing, transformations … are all examples of geometry.

Graphing

Taking a set of numbers or information and creating a visual representation of the data.

Example: (-2, -5), (-1, -4), (0, -3), (1, -2), (2, -1)

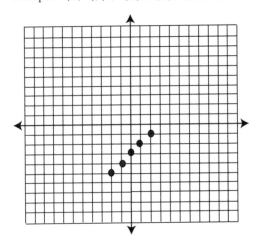

Greater than (>)

A quantity that is larger than another quantity.

Example: $9 > 2$ Nine is greater than two.

Greater than or equal to (≥)

A quantity that is larger than or equal to another quantity.

Example: 12 ≥ 6   Twelve is greater than or equal to six.
            -3 ≥ -3   Negative three is greater than or equal to negative three.

Greatest Common Factor (GCF)

The largest factor common that two or more numbers share.

Example:

Factors of 18: 1, 2, 3, 6, 9, 18
Factors of 24: 1, 2, 3, 4, 6, 8, 12, 24.
The greatest common factor of 18 and 24 is 6.

GST

A 6% federal tax (Goods and Services Tax) added on to the price of an item.

Example: $35 × 0.06 = $2.10

            The GST on an item costing $35 is $2.10.

H

Half

A quantity divided into two equal pieces.

Example: Half of 44 is 22 (44 ÷ 2 = 22).

Halves

Two identical quantities or shapes that when put together make one whole.

Example:

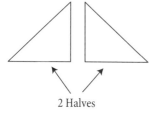
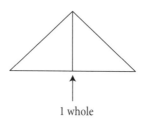

2 Halves   1 whole

Hectare
Common unit used to measure land. One hectare (1 ha) is equivalent to 1 hm^2 or 10 000 m^2 (about the size of two football fields).

Example:

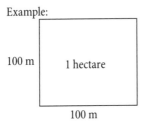

100 m   1 hectare

100 m

Height
How tall an object is. Height is found by taking the perpendicular distance from the base of an object to its highest point.

Example:

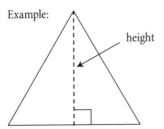

height

Heptagon
A geometric figure with seven sides.

Example:

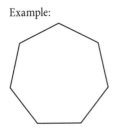

Hexagon
A geometric figure with six sides.

Example:

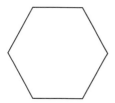

Histogram
A bar graph in which the bars are touching; a visual representation of continuous data or intervals of data.

Example:

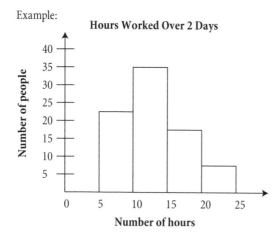

Horizontal
A line or object that is parallel to the horizon; travelling left to right.

Example:

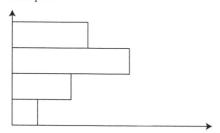

The bars in this graph are *horizontal*.

Horizontal axis

A horizontal line of reference in a graph or object.

Example:

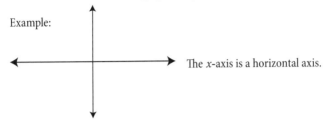

The x-axis is a horizontal axis.

Hundredth

A place value used in decimals; the second place value to the right of a decimal point.

Example: 3.527

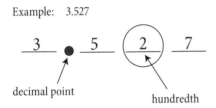

decimal point

hundredth

Hypotenuse

The side in a right triangle that is opposite the ninety degree angle. The hypotenuse is the longest side in a right triangle.

Example:

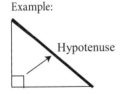

Hypotenuse

I

Image

The "new" shape that results from a transformation of the original object.

Example:

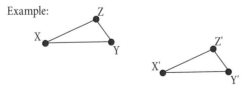

△ X'Y'Z' is the image of △ XYZ after a translation occurred.

Improper fraction

A fraction in which the numerator is greater than or equal to the denominator. Improper fractions are greater than or equal to one whole.

Example: $\frac{5}{2}$ is an improper fraction because 5 > 2.

Independent events

Two or more events in which the outcome of one event has no impact of the outcome of another event.

Example: Rolling a 5 on a dice and flipping a tail on a coin. The outcome of the dice has no impact on the outcome of the coin.

Independent variable

A variable whose value may be freely chosen and does not rely on the value of another variable.

Example: In the relationship between "pay" and "hours", hours worked is the independent variable. The amount of hours worked doesn't depend on the pay; pay depends on the number of hours worked.

Inequality

A mathematical statement comparing two values using the symbols >, <, ≥, or ≤.

Example: $4 < 6$ Four is less than six.

$x \geq 8$ An unknown value is greater than or equal to eight.

Infinity

Continuing forever without end.

Example:

The arrows on the end of a line segment show a line that extends to infinity in both directions.

Inner scale

The inside set of numbers on a protractor; used to measure angles that open from right to left.

Example:

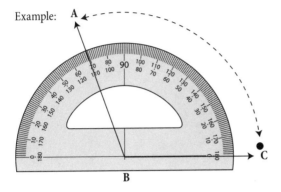

Integer

Whole numbers that are positive or negative and the number zero. The set of integers is indicated by I or Z.

Example: {…-3, -2. –1, 0, 1, 2, 3….}

Interest

The amount of money the bank pays you for the use of your money, or the amount of money you pay the bank for the use of its money.

Example: The bank pays you 4% interest on any amount in a savings account. If you have $100 in your account, you will receive $4 interest ($100 \times 0.04$).

Interior angles on the same side of the transversal

Angles formed on the inside of parallel lines, but on the same side of the transversal. Also known as co-interior angles.

Example: ∠3 and ∠5 are interior angles on the same side of the transversal as are ∠4 and ∠6.

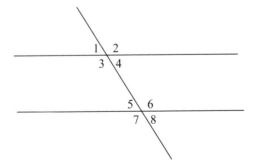

Interpolate

To estimate values within the range the given values.

Example:

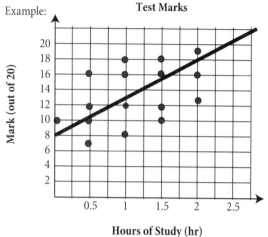

If you study for $\frac{3}{4}$ of an hour you would get a mark of about 12 out of 20.

This is an example of interpolation because the estimate falls within the range of values.

Intersecting lines

Lines that meet or touch at a common point.

Example:

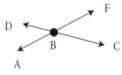

 $\overleftrightarrow{DC}$ intersects $\overleftrightarrow{AF}$ at point B.

Inverse operation

The opposite of any given operation; an operation that "undoes" another operation.

Example:

Operation	Inverse Operation
+	−
−	+
×	÷
÷	×

Irrational numbers

The set of numbers that cannot be written in the form $\frac{a}{b}$ where b ≠ 0. Irrational numbers, denoted by the letter $\overline{Q}$, include non-repeating non-ending decimals, Pi and the square roots of non-perfect squares.

Example: $\sqrt{7}$, 0.121121112… and π are examples of irrational numbers.

Isosceles triangle

A triangle that has two sides of equal length.

Example:

K

Kilometre

A common unit to measure linear distances. 1 kilometre is equivalent to 1000 metres.

Example: The distance between Calgary and Edmonton is 276 km.

Kite

A quadrilateral in which pairs of adjacent sides are congruent and no sides are parallel.

Example:

L

Legs of a right triangle

The vertical and horizontal sides of a right triangle; the sides that form the right angle.

Example: Horizontal Leg

Vertical Leg

Length

The horizontal distance from one point to another.

Example:

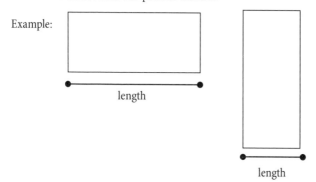

length

length

Less than (<)

A quantity that is smaller than another quantity.

Example: $2 < 9$ Two is less than nine.

Less than or equal to (≤)

A quantity that is smaller than or equal to another quantity.

Example: $6 \leq 12$ Six is less than or equal to twelve.
$-3 \leq -3$ Negative three is less than or equal to negative three.

Like fractions

Fractions that have the same denominator.

Example: $\dfrac{1}{5}$ and $\dfrac{4}{5}$ are like fractions.

Like terms

Terms that have identical variables raised to identical exponents.

Example: $2c$, c, and $-8c$ are like terms.
$2c^2$, $3cd$ and $-7c$ are not like terms.

Line

A set of points that form a straight path extending infinitely in opposite directions.

Example:

A   B

Line AB is denoted as $\overleftrightarrow{AB}$

Line of best fit

The line of best fit is the line that is as close as possible to all the data points. It does not have to pass through any of the points and it does not have to have an equal number of points above and below the line; one point a great distance above the line could be balanced by two or three points that are closer to, but below, the line.

Example:

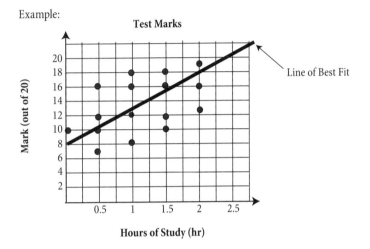

Line segment

Two fixed points that are connected; part of a line.

Example:

Line segment AB is denoted as $\overline{AB}$.

Lines of symmetry

Lines which divide a figure into two identical mirror halves.

Example:

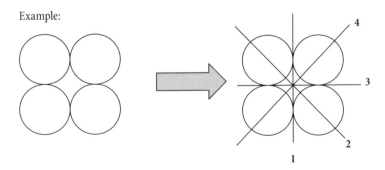

There are four lines of symmetry.

Linear
Points or objects that follow the path of a straight line.

Example: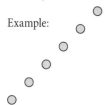

Litre
A common unit to measure volume or capacity. 1 litre is equivalent to 1 000 millilitres. It is the capacity of a cube that is 10 cm on a side.

Example: Plastic jugs of milk are sold in 1 L and 2 L sizes.

Lowest common denominator (LCD)
The smallest multiple shared among the denominators of two or more fractions.

Example: $\frac{1}{2}$ and $\frac{1}{5}$ have a lowest common denominator of 10.

Lowest Common Multiple (LCM)
The smallest multiple shared among two or more numbers.

Example: Multiples of 4: 4, 8, 12, 16, **20**, 24, 28, 32, 36, 40 …
Multiples of 10: 10, **20**, 30, 40, 50, 60 …

The lowest common multiple of 4 and 10 is 20.

Lowest terms
A ratio that contains the smallest whole number terms possible; a ratio that does not have common factors among any of the terms (other than 1).

Example: 4: 5: 8 is in lowest terms because 4, 5 and 8 have no common factors.

A fraction that does not have common factors among the numerator and denominator (other than 1).

Example: $\frac{2}{3}$ is in simplest form because 2 and 3 have no common factors.

M

Manipulated variable
A variable whose value relies (depends) on the value of another variable (independent variable).

Example: In testing the growth of plants, the height of the plant depends on the amount the plant was watered. Growth would be the manipulated variable.

Map

A scale drawing showing the ratio of map distance to land distance on Earth.

Example:

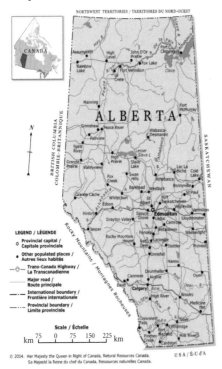

Mapping notation

Describing the transformation of an object point by point; starting with the original coordinates, add, subtract, multiply or divide each number by a value to obtain the coordinates of the image points.

Example: $(x, y) \longrightarrow (x - 2, y + 3)$

Starting with the original coordinates, subtract two from the x-value and add three to the y-value.

Markdown

A reduction in the price of an item.

Example: A shirt with a regular price of $45 was marked down to $20 because it was defective.

Markup
An increase in the price of an item.

Example: The factory price of a car was $15 000 and the dealership marked up the price to $18 000 to make a profit.

Mass
The mass of an object is a measure of the amount of matter contained in it. Mass is commonly measured in units of grams, kilograms and tons.

Example: The human brain has an average mass of 1 300 g - 1 400 g.

Maximum mat plan
The largest number of blocks that could be used to build a model without changing the base plan. The maximum mat plan is found by taking the sum of the entries in the elevation view.

Example:

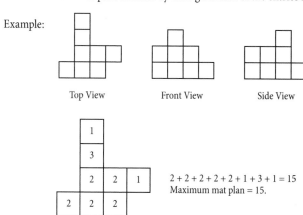

Top View   Front View   Side View

$2 + 2 + 2 + 2 + 2 + 1 + 3 + 1 = 15$
Maximum mat plan = 15.

Mean
The arithmetic average of a set of numbers found by taking the sum of a set of numbers and dividing it by the number of items in the set.

Example: {3, 7, 17, 33}
The sum of the set (60) ÷ the number of items in the set (4) = 15.
The mean is 15.

Measure of central tendency
A point within the range of a data set about which the data is thought to be balanced. There are three commonly used measures of central tendency: mean, median, and mode.

Example: 56   82   42   95   67   75   34   77
          66   71   74   68   80   82   45   90

The measures of central tendency are: mean of 69, median of 72.5 and mode of 82.

Median

of data: The middle number of a set of numbers. It is found by ordering the numbers in the set from smallest to largest and finding the middle.

     Example: The median of {2, 7, 15, 56, 89} is 15 because it is the middle number of the set of data.

of a triangle: A line segment drawn from the vertex of an object to the midpoint of the opposite side.

     Example:

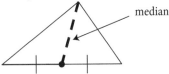

Metre

A common unit to measure linear distances. 1 metre is equivalent to 100 centimetres.

     Example: The average height of a giraffe is 4.6 – 5.5 m.

Midpoint

The half-way point of a line segment.

     Example:

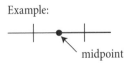

Minimum mat plan

The smallest number of blocks that could be used to build a model without changing the base plan. The minimum mat plan is found by taking the sum of the entries in the elevation view.

     Example:

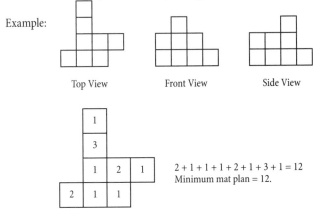

Top View   Front View   Side View

2 + 1 + 1 + 1 + 2 + 1 + 3 + 1 = 12
Minimum mat plan = 12.

Minuend

The number another number is subtracted from; the first number in a subtraction sentence.

Example: $3 - 2$
"3" is the minuend.

Mixed number

The sum of a whole number and a fraction.

Example: $5\frac{2}{3}$ is a mixed number because it has a whole number (5) and fraction ($\frac{2}{3}$).

Mode

The number that occurs most often in a set of numbers. There can be more than one mode.

Example: 45, 56, 75, 75, 80
The mode is 75.

Monomial

An algebraic expression or polynomial with one term.

Example: 2, x,$-3c$ and $12p^2q^3$ are all monomials.

Multiple

The product of two natural numbers in any given order.

Example: Multiples of 5
$5 \times 1 = 5$
$5 \times 2 = 10$
$5 \times 3 = 15$
$5 \times 4 = 20$
$5 \times 5 = 25$
$5 \times 6 = 30 \ldots$

Multiplicand

Term(s) used in a multiplication equation.

Example: 7×8
"7" and "8" are the multiplicands.

N

Natural numbers

Sometimes called the "counting numbers", natural numbers are positive whole numbers starting with the number one and increasing by increments of one.

Example: $N = \{1, 2, 3, 4 \ldots\}$

Negative
A number that is less than 0.

    Example: {-1, -2, -3, -4 ...}

Negative exponent
A power with an exponent that is less than zero in value; if the base has a numeric value less than one, the value of a power with a negative exponent will be greater than one and vice versa.

    Example: 4^{-3}

        "-3" is the negative exponent. Since the base (4) is greater than one, 4^{-3} will have a value less than one. $4^{-3} = (\frac{1}{4})^{+3} = \frac{1}{64} = 0.015\ 625$.

        $(\frac{1}{2})^{-4}$

        "-4" is the negative exponent. Since the base $(\frac{1}{2})$ is less than one, $(\frac{1}{2})^{-4}$ will have a value greater than one. $(\frac{1}{2})^{-4} = (\frac{2}{1})^{+4} = 2^{+4} = 16$.

Negative relationship
A relationship between two variables whereby the value of one variable decreases as the value of another variable increases. A negative relationship can be illustrated in a scatter plot where the points slope down and left.

    Example:

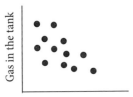

    This is a "negative relationship" because as the distance travelled increases, the amount of gas in the tank decreases.

Net
A flat diagram of two-dimensional faces arranged so that the diagram may be folded to form a three dimensional solid

    Example:

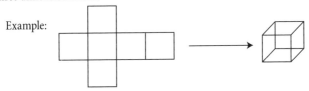

    This is a net for a cube.

Network

A diagram made up of line segments and/or arcs that intersect at one or more points.

Example:

No relationship or no correlation

Two variables that do not have a connection or influence on one another. Graphically, if there is no relationship, the points of the scatter plot would have no pattern.

Example:

This is an example of "no relationship" because the height of a tree has no influence or impact on the distance travelled.

Nonagon

A polygon with nine sides.

Example:

Neutral number

A number that is neither positive or negative.

Example: 0 is the only neutral number.
Numbers above 0 are positive.
Numbers below 0 are negative.

Number line

A horizontal or vertical line that shows the placement of numbers in the real number system.

Example:

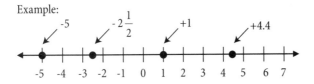

Numerator

The top number in the fraction; it shows the number of parts of a whole or the number of items in a set.

Example: $\dfrac{2}{3}$ "2" is the numerator.

O

Obtuse angle

An angle that measures between 90° and 180°.

Example:

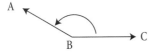

$\angle ABC$ is an obtuse angle.

Obtuse triangle

A triangle that has one obtuse angle.

Example:

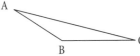

$\triangle ABC$ is an obtuse triangle.

Octagon

A polygon with eight sides.

Example:

Odd number
A number that is not divisible by two.

Example: 15 is an odd number because it is not divisible by 2 (15 ÷ 2 = 7, remainder 1).

Odd vertices
A point at which an odd number of line segments or arcs meet.

Example:

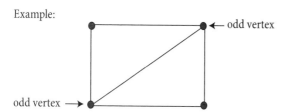

Of
In mathematics, "of" can imply multiplication.

Example: Half of ten means to multiply $\frac{1}{2}$ by 10.
Half of ten is five ($\frac{1}{2} \times 10 = 5$).

Opposite angles
Pairs of angles that are formed when two lines intersect. These angles are mirror images of one another and therefore are congruent.

Example: ∡1 and ∡3 are opposite angles and ∡2 and ∡4 are opposite angles.

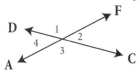

Opposite integers
Integers that have the same numeric value but opposite signs. 0 does not have an opposite as it is neither positive nor negative.

Example: +7 and -7 are opposite integers.

-8 and +8 are opposite integers.

Opposite side

Sides that do not have a common vertex.

Example:

$\overline{AB}$ is opposite of $\overline{DC}$ because they do not share any vertices.

Or

In mathematics, "or" is inclusive; one event or another event or both events together.

Example: Sample space for rolling a three = {3}
Sample space for rolling an even = {2, 4, 6}
Sample space for rolling a three OR an even = {2, 3, 4, 6}

Order

A specific sequence or arrangement of numbers or objects.

Example: $-3.5, -2, -\dfrac{1}{5}, 0, 3.\overline{4}, 5\dfrac{2}{5}$
The numbers are in order from smallest to largest.

Order of operations

An established order to follow when three or more mathematical operations are performed. The acronym BEDMAS is often used to help with memory recall of the order.

Example:

Steps	Operation
$3^2 \div (-3) \times 2 - (1 \times -7)$	Brackets
$3^2 \div (-3) \times 2 - (-7)$	Exponents
$9 \div (-3) \times 2 - (-7)$	Division
$-3 \times 2 - (-7)$	Multiplication
$-6 - (-7)$	Subtraction
$-6 + (+7)$	Addition
$+1$	

Ordered pairs

Pairs of numbers that describe the location of a point on the coordinate plane compared to the origin.

Example: (-2, 5) is the coordinate 2 units left and 5 units up from the origin.

Ordering powers

To place powers in a specific sequence (small to big or big to small) according to their value in standard form.

Example: 2^2, 4^2, 5^2, 3^3 are arranged in ascending order.

Origin

The point at which the x axis and the y axis intersect; the origin has coordinates of (0,0).

Example:

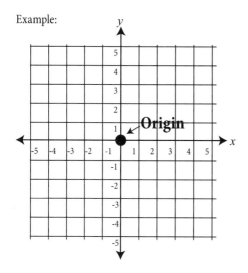

Original

A shape or object before a change or transformation has occurred.

Example:

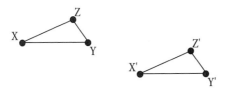

$\triangle$ XYZ is the original shape before the translation occurs.

Outcome

The result of an event occurring.

Example: The outcome of rolling a die is {1, 2, 3, 4, 5, 6}.

Outer scale

The outside set of numbers on a protractor; used to measure angles that open from left to right.

Example:

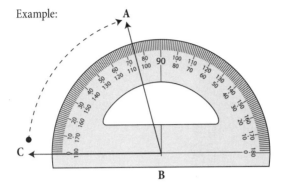

Outlier

A data value that is substantially larger or smaller than the other values

Example: 10, 12, 17, 22, 25, 33, 35, 36, 89, 91

outliers

P

Parallel

Travelling in the same direction and always an equal distance apart.

Example:

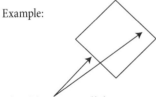

The sides are parallel.

Parallel lines

Lines that travel in the same direction and never intersect.

Example:

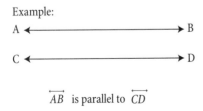

A ⟵————————————⟶ B

C ⟵————————————⟶ D

$\overleftrightarrow{AB}$ is parallel to $\overleftrightarrow{CD}$

Parallelogram
A four-sided polygon with opposite sides parallel and equal in length.

Example:

Pattern
A repeated order or sequence of numbers or objects.

Example: 1, 5, 9, 13, 17, 21 ... The pattern to the set of numbers is to add four to the previous number.

Pentagon
A polygon with five sides.

Example:

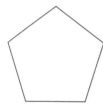

Percent
A ratio or fraction with 100 as the second term or denominator.

Example: 50% means 50 out of one hundred. Percent means per hundred.

Perfect square
A number that has two identical factors that are whole numbers; the square of a whole number.

Example: 16 is a perfect square because it has two identical factors ($16 = 4 \times 4 = 4^2$).

Perimeter
The distance around the outside of a polygon.

Example:

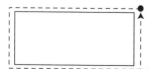

Perpendicular
Meeting at a 90° angle.

Example:

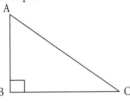

$\overline{AB}$ is perpendicular to $\overline{BC}$.
$\overline{AB} \perp \overline{BC}$

Perpendicular lines
Lines that intersect at a 90° angle.

Example:

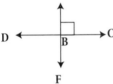

$\overleftrightarrow{AF}$ is perpendicular to $\overleftrightarrow{DC}$.
$\overleftrightarrow{AF} \perp \overleftrightarrow{DC}$.

Pi (π)
The ratio of a circle's circumference of any circle to its diameter is Pi. The approximate value of Pi is 3.14.

Example: The circle below has a circumference of 14.13 m and a diameter of 4.5 m.

$$\frac{C}{d} = \frac{14.13}{4.5}$$

$$\frac{C}{d} = 3.14$$

The ratio of the circumference and the diameter is 3.14, the approximate value of Pi.

Pictograph

A graph that uses pictures or symbols to represent quantities in similar groups.

Example:

Top Burger Choices	
MacDonalds's	☺☺☺☺☺☺☺☺☺
Wendy's	☺☺☺☺
Burger King	☺☺☺☺☺☺☺
Harvey's	☺
Each ☺ represents 5 students	

Place value

Connects a digit to its corresponding position within the number.

Example: 400 000
"4" is in the hundred thousands place.
Its place value is four hundred thousands.

Plane of symmetry

A two-dimensional plane that cuts a 3-dimensional shape into two symmetrical halves.

Example: A rectangular prism has 3 planes of symmetry.

Point

Identifies a position. It is represented by a dot.

Example: ●
B

Polygon

A two dimensional closed figure with three or more straight side lengths.

Example:

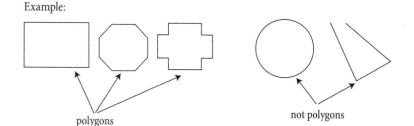

polygons

not polygons

Polyhedron

A three-dimensional object with two dimensional faces. It has no curved regions or edges.

Example:

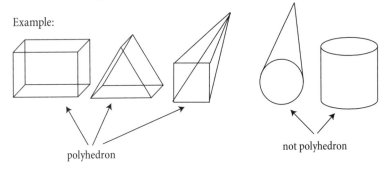

polyhedron

not polyhedron

Polynomial

A sum and/or difference of algebraic terms.

Example: "$3x + 3$", "$4x^2y$", "$2x^3y^2 - 3xy^3 - 4$" are all polynomials.

Population

A group of people or items from which data could be collected.

Example: One marble is to be drawn randomly from a bag of marbles. The population would be all the marbles in the bag.

Positive

A number that is greater than 0.

Example: $\{1, 2, 3, 4 \dots\}$

Positive exponent

A power with an exponent that is greater than zero in value.

Example: 4^3 "3" is the positive exponent.

Positive relationship

A relationship between two variables whereby the value of one variable increases as the value of the other variable increases. A positive relationship can be illustrated in a scatter plot where the points slope up and right.

Example:

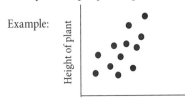

This is a "positive relationship" because as the amount of rainfall increases, the height of the plant also increases.

Power

A number raised to an exponent. Powers are named by their bases.

Example: 2^6 is "the sixth power of 2".

Power laws

a. Power of a Power
    Used to simplify a power raised to an exponent; keep the base the same and multiply the exponents.

    Example: $(x^a)^b = x^{a \times b}$ $(2^3)^4 = 2^{12}$

b. Power of a Product Law
    Used to multiply powers with different bases but the same exponent; multiply the bases and keep the exponent the same.

    Example: $(x^a)(y^a) = (x \times y)^a$ $(4^2)(6^2) = 24^2$

c. Power of a Quotient Law
    Used to divide powers with different bases but the same exponent; divide the bases, and keep the exponent the same.

    Example: $\dfrac{x^a}{y^a} = \left(\dfrac{x}{y}\right)^a$ $\dfrac{27^4}{3^4} = 9^4$

d. Zero Exponent
    Used to simplify powers with an exponent of zero; any non-zero base raised to an exponent of zero equals one.

    Example: $x^0 = 1$ $(x \neq 0)$ $5^0 = 1$ Note: 0^0 is undefined. $0^0 = \emptyset = \{\ \}$

e. Negative Exponents
    Used to simplify powers with negative exponents; take the reciprocal of the base and raise it to a positive exponent.

    Example: $(x)^{-n} = \left(\dfrac{1}{x}\right)^n$ $(5)^{-3} = \left(\dfrac{1}{5}\right)^3$

f. Product Law
    Used to multiply powers with the same base; keep the base the same and add the exponents.

    Example: $(x^a)(x^b) = x^{a+b}$ $(2^4)(2^2) = 2^6$

g. Quotient Law
    Used to divide powers with the same base; keep the base the same and subtract the exponents

    Example: $\dfrac{x^a}{x^b} = x^{a-b}$ $\dfrac{3^5}{3^2} = 3^3$

Powers of ten

A base of ten raised to a positive or negative exponent; powers of ten are used in scientific notation.

Example: 10^4 is a power of ten meaning $10 \times 10 \times 10 \times 10$ or 10 000.

10^{-3} is a power of ten meaning $\dfrac{1}{10} \times \dfrac{1}{10} \times \dfrac{1}{10} = \dfrac{1}{1000}$ or 0.001.

Prime

An accent mark used to label the vertices of an object that has undergone a transformation; the number of accent marks indicates the number of transformations an object has gone through.

Example:

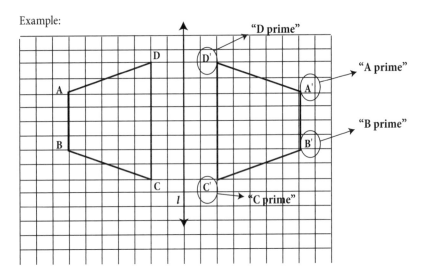

Prime factor

A prime number that another number is divisible by.

Example: "2" is a prime factor of 6 because 2 is a prime number and 6 is divisible by 2.

Prime factorization

To write a number as a product of its prime factors.

Example: $20 = 2 \times 2 \times 5$ or $20 = 2^2 \times 5$

Prime number

A number that has exactly two unique factors.

Example: 5 is a prime number because its only factors are 1 and 5.

Principal
The amount of money you deposit or borrow.

    Example: You borrow $20 000 to buy a car; the principal is $20 000.
                   You invest $5 000 into an RRSP; the principal is $5 000.

Prism
A three-dimensional object with two parallel and congruent sides and all remaining sides are rectangles or parallelograms.

    Example:

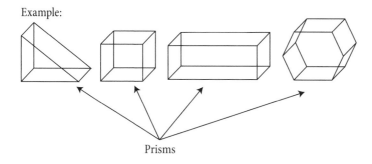

Prisms

Probability
The likelihood an event will occur; the ratio of favorable outcomes to total outcomes.

    Example: $P(\text{Heads}) = \dfrac{1}{2}$
                 The probability of flipping a coin and it landing on heads is 1 (head) out of 2 (sides of the coin).

                 $P(\text{Even}) = \dfrac{3}{6} \longrightarrow \dfrac{1}{2}$
                 The probability of rolling a die and it landing on an even number is 3 (3 even numbers on a die: 2, 4, 6) out of 6 (sides of the die). In probability all fractions must be placed in lowest terms.

Product
The result of two or more numbers multiplied together; the answer to a multiplication sentence.

    Example: The product of five and six is thirty.

Proper fraction
A fraction in which the numerator is smaller than the denominator.

    Example: $\dfrac{4}{7}$ is a proper fraction because 4 < 7.

Proportion

An equation that shows two equivalent ratios.

Example: $1 : 4 = 2 : 8$

This is a proportion because each ratio has the same value; they both simplify to $1 : 4$.

$$\frac{8}{14} = \frac{12}{21}$$

This is a proportion because each fraction has the same value; they both simplify to $\frac{4}{7}$.

Protractor

An instrument used to measure angles by lining up the rays of the angle and reading the distance between the two rays which is measured in degrees; each marking on a protractor represents one degree.

Example:

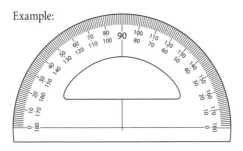

Pyramid

A three-dimensional object with a polygon base and triangular faces. Pyramids come to a point at the top.

Example:

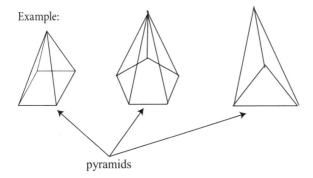

pyramids

Pythagorean theorem

A relationship among the side lengths of a right triangle whereby the length of the hypotenuse squared (c^2) equals the length of the horizontal leg squared (a^2) added to the length of the vertical leg squared (b^2).
$a^2 + b^2 = c^2$

Example:

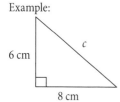

$$a^2 + b^2 = c^2$$
$$8^2 + 6^2 = c^2$$
$$64 + 36 = c^2$$
$$100 = c^2$$
$$10 = c$$

Q

Quadrants

The four areas formed when the x-axis and y-axis intersect on a Cartesian plane.

Example:

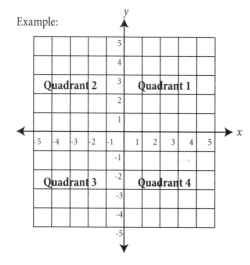

Quadrilateral

A polygon with four sides and four angles.

Example:

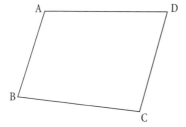

ABCD is a quadrilateral.

Quartiles
The three values that split a set of data into 4 equal groups

Example:

13   14   (17)   18   19   (20)   23   27   (29)   30   35

Quartile 1   Quartile 2   Quartile 3
                    (Median)

Questionnaire
A printed set of questions used to gather information from people.

Example:

1. Of the following list of music, which type do you like best?

   a. Country
   b. Classical
   c. Rap
   d. Rock and Roll
   e. Top 40

2. Of the following vending machine choices, which do you like best?

   a. Chips
   b. Chocolate Bars
   c. Gum
   d. Granola Bars
   e. Mints

Quotient
The result of dividing two numbers; the answer to a division question.

Example: $21 \div 7 = 3$

"3" is the quotient.

R

Radical
The symbol used to represent the positive square root of a number.

Example: $\sqrt{16} = 4$

"$\sqrt{}$" is the radical, also known as the principal square root.

Radius
The distance from the centre of a circle to any point on the circle.

Example:

radius

Range
How spread out a set of data is; the difference between the highest and lowest values.

Example: 33, 45, 45, 48, 49, 52, 64, 66, 72, 77

The range is 44 (77 – 33).

Rate
A comparison of two or more quantities with different units.

Example: 35 words/minute

This is a rate because "words" and "minutes" are different types of units.

Rate of interest
The percentage of the principal you pay or receive in interest charges.

Example: The bank pays 4% interest on any amount in a savings account. "4%" is the rate of interest.

Ratio
A comparison of two or more quantities with the same units.

Example: 17 boys to 14 girls

"17 to 14" is a ratio because both quantities have the same unit (number of people).

Rational numbers
The set of numbers that can be written in the form $\frac{a}{b}$ where b ≠ 0. Rational numbers, denoted by the letter Q, include natural numbers, whole numbers, integers, fractions repeating decimals and terminating decimals.

Example: "$\frac{4}{-9}$", "$0.\overline{7}$", "-4", "0.23", "$\sqrt{4}$", "5", "$2\frac{1}{2}$", "$\frac{23}{100}$" are examples of rational numbers.

Ray

Starting at a fixed end point and extending infinitely in one direction; part of a line.

Example:

A   B

$\overrightarrow{AB}$ is a ray.

Real number

The set of rational and irrational numbers. The real number system is denoted by the letter $\Re$.

Example: "$\dfrac{4}{-9}$", "-4", "0.23", "$\sqrt{4}$", "5", "$2\dfrac{1}{2}$", "$\dfrac{23}{100}$", "$\sqrt{7}$", "$0.\overline{4}$", "0.121121112…", "π" are examples of real numbers

Reciprocal

Two numbers whose product is 1 are said to be reciprocals.

Example: The reciprocal of 3 is $\dfrac{1}{3}$.

The reciprocal of $\dfrac{2}{3}$ is $\dfrac{3}{2}$.

Rectangle

A four-sided polygon with four right angles and opposite sides equal in length.

Example:

ABCD is a rectangle.

Rectangular prism

A three-dimensional object with two dimensional faces rectangular in shape.

Example:

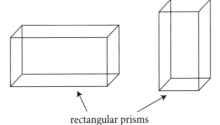

rectangular prisms

Reduction

A transformation in which an object is made smaller. The image is smaller than the actual object.

Example:

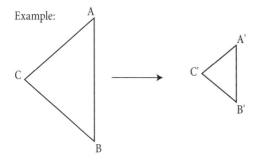

Reflection

A transformation in which a figure is flipped about a line of reference called the reflection line.

Example:

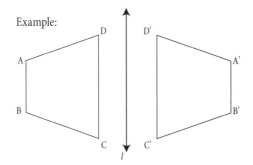

ABCD has been reflected about line *l*. The image, after reflection, is A'B'C'D'. The points in ABCD are the same distance from the reflection line as the corresponding points in A'B'C'D'.

Reflection line

A mirror line about which an object is reflected; points in the original figure are equal distance to the reflection line as points in the image figure.

Example:

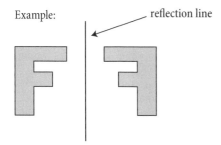

reflection line

Reflex angle
An angle that measures between 180° and 360°.

Example:

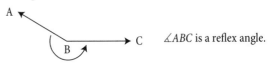

$\angle ABC$ is a reflex angle.

Regular polygon
A polygon with all sides equal in length and with all angles congruent.

Example:

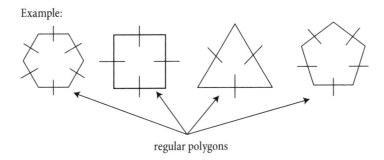

regular polygons

Regular price
The price of an item without any deductions in price.

Example: The price of a shirt is $14.99.

Relation
The connection or relationship between a set of numbers. Relations can be represented with words, ordered pairs, graphs, table of values and equations.

Example: The following all represent the relation "a number increased by two is another number".

1. $y = x + 2$

2. $(-2, 0)$ $(-1, 1)$ $(0, 2)$ $(1, 3)$ $(2, 4)$

3.

-2	0
-1	1
0	2
1	3
2	4

4.

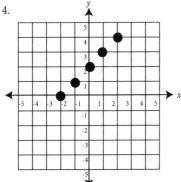

Remainder
The number left over after a number is divided by another number.

Example: The remainder when 7 is divided by 2 is 1.

$$2)\overline{7}$$ with quotient 3

1 ← remainder

Repeating decimal
A decimal that has one or more digits that repeats without end.

Example: "$0.\overline{7}$", "0.3333...", "$2.\overline{2}$" and "$0.\overline{213}$" are all repeating decimals.

Rhombus
A parallelogram with four equal sides.

Example:

ABCD is a rhombus.

Right angle
An angle that measures exactly 90°.

Example:

$\angle ABC$ is a right angle.

Right triangle

A triangle with one angle measuring 90°.

Example:

$\angle ABC$ is a right triangle because $\angle B$ is 90°.

Root

One of two identical factors of a number.

Example: $16 = 4 \times 4$ The root of 16 is 4.

Rotation

A transformation in which an object is turned clockwise or counterclockwise around a fixed point.

Example:

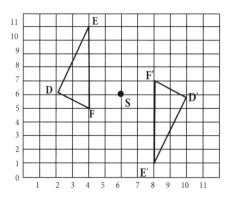

ΔDEF has been rotated 180° around point S, the rotation centre. ΔD'E'F' is the image after the rotation has occurred.

Round

Rewriting an exact number as an approximate value to an indicated place.

Example: Round 1 476 to the nearest ten.
                1 476 is in-between 1 470 and 1480 but closer to 1 480.
                Therefore, 1 476 rounded to the nearest ten is 1 480.

Row
Arranged horizontally; in a table, numbers that can be read left to right.

Example:

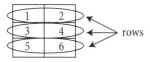

This table has three rows.

S

Sale price
The price you will pay for an item after a discount has been applied.
Sale price = regular price – discount

Example: A sweater regularly costs $35.99. A discount of $3.50 means the sale price of
the sweater is $32.49 (35.99 – 3.50).

Sample
A smaller group of people or things taken from a larger population; samples are used to test
and make generalizations about the entire population.

Example: Wanting to know what music Grade 8 students in your school like,
(population = all grade 8 students in your school), four Grade 8 students
from each class were surveyed at random (sample = four students from each
class).

Sample size
The total number of outcomes for an event.

Example: Rolling a die has a sample size of 6 as there are 6 possible outcomes
(1, 2, 3, 4, 5, 6).

Flipping a coin has a sample size of 2 as there are 2 possible outcomes
(Heads, Tails).

Sample Space
A list of all possible outcomes for an event; { } are used to show all the outcomes in the
sample space.

Example: Flipping a coin: {Heads, Tails}
Rolling a die: {1, 2, 3, 4, 5, 6}

SAS

A congruency theorem which states "if two sides and their included angle of one triangle are equal in measurement to two corresponding sides and their included angle of another triangle, the triangles are congruent".

Example:

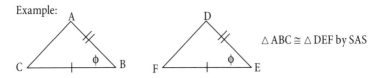

△ ABC ≅ △ DEF by SAS

Scale

The ratio length of an image to length of an actual object.

Example: The map scale is 1: 1 000 000.

This means 1 cm on the map represents 1 000 000 cm (1 km) of land distance.

Scale drawing

An accurate drawing that either proportionally enlarges or proportionally reduces the size of an actual object.

Example: A map is a scale drawing.

Scale factor

The ratio of scale size to actual size.

Example: A scale factor of $\frac{1}{5}$ means 1 unit in the scale object represents 5 units in the actual object (i.e. the image is $\frac{1}{5}$ the size of the original and therefore a reduction).

A scale factor of 3 (or $\frac{3}{1}$) means 3 units in the scale object represents 1 unit in the actual object (i.e. the image is 3 times the size of the original and therefore an enlargement).

Scalene triangle

A triangle in which no two sides have the same measure; all three sides have a different length.

Example:

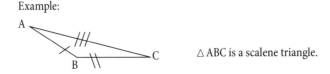

△ ABC is a scalene triangle.

Scatter plot

A graph in which a pair of variables is represented by a point; the collection of points shows the relationship between two variables.

Example: The scatter plot shows the relationship between hours of study and the results on a test.

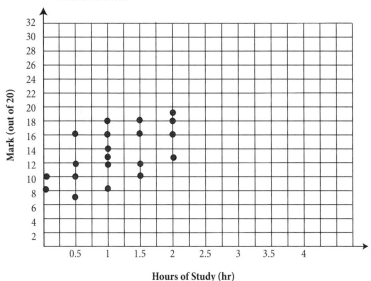

Scientific notation

A condensed way of writing very large or very small numbers; a decimal number in between 1 and 10 is multiplied by a power of ten.

Example: 12 500 000 written in scientific notation is 1.25×10^7.

0.000 000 045 written in scientific notation is 4.5×10^{-8}.

Set

A collection of numbers or items with similar characteristics.

Example: {1, 2, 3, 4...} is the set of whole numbers.

{square, rhombus, rectangle, parallelogram, kite, trapezoid} is the set of quadrilaterals.

Sign

Either positive or negative.

Example: The sign of -4 is negative.

The sign of +5 is positive, as is 5 (+5 = 5).

Similar triangles

Triangles that have the same shape but not necessarily the same size; triangles in which all the angles are equal and the side lengths are proportional.

Example:

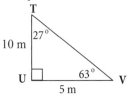

ΔTUV is similar to ΔQRS because all their angles are equal and the sides are in porportion (The sides of ΔQRS are two-thirds the length of the corresponding sides of ΔTUV).

Simplest form

When the numerator and denominator of a fraction have no common factors, other than 1.

Example: $\frac{2}{3}$ is in simplest form because 2 and 3 have no common factors other than 1.

Simulation

A model or experiment used to reproduce results of another event; a way of calculating experimental probability. Also known as the Monte Carlo method.

Example: Wanting to know what the likelihood of passing a 10 question True/False quiz by guessing, a coin was flipped 10 times and the results were recorded. If "Tails" represented getting a question correct by guessing, the number of times tails appeared would be the number of questions answered correct by guessing.
Flipping the coin is a simulation of writing the test.

Sine

A trigonometric ratio used in right triangles comparing the length of the side opposite a given angle to the length of the hypotenuse.

Example:

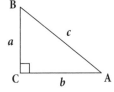 $\text{Sin } \angle A = \frac{a}{c}$ $\text{Sin } \angle B = \frac{b}{c}$

Skeleton

A three-dimensional object in which only the vertices and edges are showing.

Example:

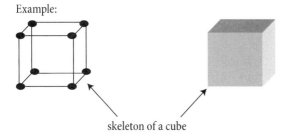

skeleton of a cube

Slant height

A line drawn from the vertex of a cone to a point on the circumference of the cone's circular base.

Example:

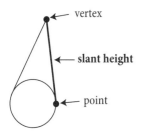

Slide

A transformation that moves an object left or right and/or up or down. Also known as a translation.

Example:

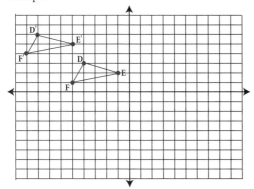

Δ *DEF* was moved 4 units left and 3 units up. Δ *D'E'F'* is the result of this slide.

SOH CAH TOA
An acronym used to remember the trigonometric ratios in a right triangle.

Example: **S**ine =
Opposite over
Hypotenuse

Cosine =
Adjacent over
Hypotenuse

Tangent =
Opposite over
Adjacent

Solid
A three dimensional object that is completely filled inside; not hollow

Example:

A stick of butter and sugar cubes are examples of solids.

Solution
The answer to a question.

Example: $x + 7 = 10$

The solution is $x = 3$

Five years ago, I was 13 years old. How old am I now?

The solution is 18 years old.

Solution set
A set of values for a variable that satisfies an equation or inequality.

Example: $n > -4$ $n \in I$
{-3, -2, -1, 0 ...} is the solution set.

Solve an algebraic equation
To find the correct value of the variable to make the equation "true" or balanced.

Example:

$$5y = 35$$
$$\frac{5y}{5} = \frac{35}{5}$$
$$y = 7$$

Solve a right triangle
To find all missing side lengths and all missing angle measurements.

Example:

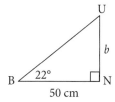

$$\frac{\tan(22^\circ)}{1} = \frac{b}{50}$$
$$b = 50\,(\text{Tan } 22^\circ)$$
$$b = 20.2 \text{ cm}$$

$$\angle U + \angle B + \angle N = 180^\circ$$
$$\angle U + 22^\circ + 90^\circ = 180^\circ$$
$$\angle U + 112^\circ = 180^\circ$$
$$\angle U = 180^\circ - 112^\circ$$
$$\angle U = 68^\circ$$

$$a^2 + b^2 = c^2$$
$$(50)^2 + (20.2)^2 = n^2$$
$$2\,908.04 = n^2$$
$$\sqrt{2908.04} = n$$
$$53.9 \text{ cm} = n$$

Square
A four-sided polygon with all sides equal in length, and all corners equal to 90°.

Example:

ABCD is a quadrilateral.

Squared
A number raised to the exponent of two.

Example: 7^2

Square root
One of two identical factors of a number.

Example: $16 = 4 \times 4$
$$\sqrt{16} = 4$$

SSS

A congruency theorem which states if three corresponding sides of one triangle are equal in measurement to three corresponding sides of another triangle, the triangles are congruent.

Example:

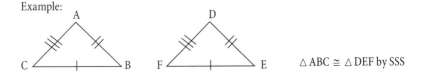

$\triangle$ ABC $\cong$ $\triangle$ DEF by SSS

Standard form

of a number: The answer to a number written in expanded form.

Example: $300\,000 + 40\,000 + 7\,000 + 7$ in standard form is 347 007.

Example: $3 \times 10^4 + 7 \times 10^2 + 8 \times 10^0$ in standard form is 30 708.

of exponents: The answer to a repeated multiplication sentence.

Example: $7 \times 7 \times 7$ in standard form is 343.

Statistics

A type of mathematics that analyzes and interprets numerical data.

Example: Mean, mode, median, range, extremes and clusters are all examples of statistics.

Stem and leaf plot

A way of organizing data into categories based on their place value; the leaf is usually the last digit of a number and the stem is the digits to the left of the leaf.

Example:

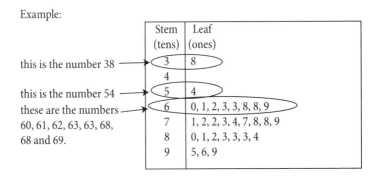

Stem (tens)	Leaf (ones)
3	8
4	
5	4
6	0, 1, 2, 3, 3, 8, 8, 9
7	1, 2, 2, 3, 4, 7, 8, 8, 9
8	0, 1, 2, 3, 3, 3, 4
9	5, 6, 9

this is the number 38
this is the number 54
these are the numbers 60, 61, 62, 63, 63, 68, 68 and 69.

Straight angle

An angle that measures exactly 180°. It is the measure of a straight line.

Example:

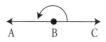

∡ABC is a straight angle.

Substitution

To replace a variable by a given number to evaluate an expression or check the solution of an equation.

Example: Evaluate $5ab - 6$ for $a = 5$ and $b = -1$.

$5ab - 6$
$5(5)(-1) - 6$ ←———————   5 is substituted for "a"
$-25 - 6$ -1 is substituted for "b"
-31

Subtrahend

The integer being subtracted from another integer; the second number in a subtraction sentence.

Example: $3 - 2$
          "2" is the subtrahend.

Sum

The result of adding numbers or quantities together; the answer to an addition sentence.

Example: $3 + 4 + 5 = 12$
          "12" is the sum.

Supplementary angle

Two angles whose sum is 180°.

Example:

$$A \longleftarrow \underset{B}{140°/40°} \longrightarrow C$$

∠ ABD and ∠ CBD are supplementary angles.

Supplementary angles that are adjacent are also known as a linear pair.
∡ABD and ∡CBD are a linear pair of angles.

Surface area

The sum of the areas of all the outside faces of a three dimensional shape.

Example:

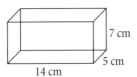

$A = l \times w$	$A = l \times w$	$A = l \times w$
$A = 14 \times 5$	$A = 14 \times 7$	$A = 5 \times 7$
$A = 70$	$A = 98$	$A = 35$
$2 \times 70 = 140$	$2 \times 98 = 196$	$2 \times 35 = 70$

$SA = 140 + 196 + 70$
$SA = 406$
The surface area is 406 cm^2.

Symmetry

Equal in shape, size and orientation about a fixed point, line or plane.

line symmetry: a figure is said to have line symmetry when it maps onto itself when reflected in a line.

Example:

This triangle has symmetry about the line. Both sides are equal in size and shape on either side of the line.

If you were to use the line as a fold line, the triangle would be two identical halves match up perfectly.

rotational symmetry: a figure is said to have rotational symmetry if it maps onto itself in less than one full turn.

Example:

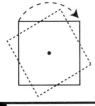

A Square is said to have rotational symmetry because it can rotate $\frac{1}{4}$ turn or 90° about its centre and map onto itself (i.e. line up with it self, corner to corner.)

T

Table of values
A table displaying the relationship between two variables.

Example:

a	a + 5		
1	6	←	(1) + 5
2	7	←	(2) + 5
3	8	←	(3) + 5
4	9	←	(4) + 5
5	10	←	(5) + 5
6	11	←	(6) + 5

Tally
Individual strokes or marks made to keep count of objects; tallies are grouped in bundles of five.

Example:

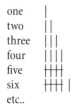

one | |
two | ||
three | |||
four | ||||
five | ||||
six | |||| |
etc..

Tally chart
A table that uses tallies to count data.

Example:

Favourite Music	Tally
Rap		
Country	||||
Jazz	||
Pop	|||
Rock	||||

Tangent

A trigonometric ratio used in right triangles comparing the opposite side to the adjacent side from a given angle's perspective.

Example:

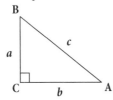

$$\text{Tan } \angle A = \frac{a}{b} \qquad \text{Tan } \angle B = \frac{b}{a}$$

Tenth

A place value used in decimals; the first place value to the right of a decimal point.

Example:

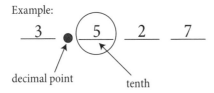

Terminating decimal

A decimal that has a fixed number of decimal places; a decimal that ends.

Example: 32.6, 0.6, 0.334 576, -3.400 02 are terminating decimals.

Terms of a ratio

Numbers or quantities measured in the same units that are compared to one another.

Example: "17:14" has two terms (17 and 14).

"5 to 4 to 3" has three terms (5, 4 and 3).

Theoretical probability

The ratio of the number of ways an event could occur to the total number of outcomes in the sample space.

$$P \text{ (event)} = \frac{\text{number of favorable outcomes}}{\text{number of possible outcomes}}$$

Example: The probability of rolling a die and it landing on a prime number:

$$P(\text{Prime}) = \frac{3}{6} \longleftarrow \begin{matrix} \text{3 prime numbers (2, 3, 5)} \\ \text{6 numbers on a die (1, 2, 3, 4, 5, 6)} \end{matrix}$$

Thousandth

A place value used in decimals; the third place value to the right of a decimal point.

Example: 3.527

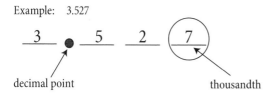

decimal point   thousandth

Total

The result of adding numbers or quantities together; the answer to an addition sentence.

Example: $3 + 4 + 5 = 23$

"12" is the total.

Traceable network

A network that can be drawn through its entire path without raising a pencil from the paper or drawing over the same line.

Example:

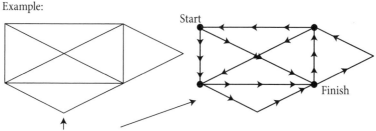

The above is a traceable network.

Transformations

Taking one geometric shape and changing to a similar geometric shape according to some rule.

Example: Rotations, translations, reflections, enlargements and reductions are all transformations.

Translation

A transformation in which each vertex of an object is moved the same distance and in the same direction.

Example:

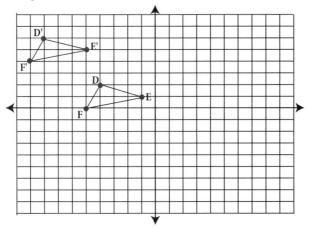

ΔDEF was translated 4 units left and 4 units up. ΔD'E'F' is the result of this translation.

Translation arrow

An arrow that shows the instructions for a translation or slide. The starting position is shown by the tail of the arrow (●) and the ending position is shown by the tip of the arrow (▶).

Example:

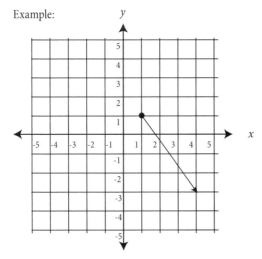

This translation arrow shows a translation of 3 right and 4 down.

Transversal
A line that intersects two or more lines.

Example:

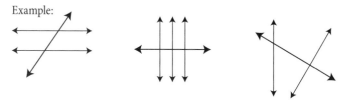

These are all transversals.

Trapezoid
A four-sided figure in which one pair of sides is parallel and the other pair of sides is not parallel.

Example:

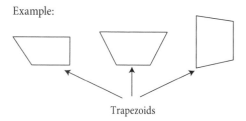

Trapezoids

Triangle
A geometric shape with three sides and three angles; a three-sided polygon.

Example:

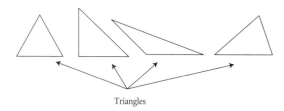

Triangles

Trigonometry
A type of mathematics that studies the relationship among sides and angles in triangles.

Example: Sine, cosine, tangent, Pythagorean theorem, calculating the missing angle in a triangle and calculating the missing side in a triangle are all examples of trigonometry.

Trinomial

An algebraic expression or polynomial with three terms.

Example: "$3x^2y - 3x + 4$" and "$3x^2y + 3y - x$" are trinomials.

True statement

A statement that is correct.

Example: $x = 2$ in the equation $x + 4 = 6$

$$x + 4 = 6$$
$$(2) + 4 = 6$$
$$6 = 6$$

A true statement was reached ($6 = 6$) therefore $x = 2$ is the solution.

Turn

A transformation in which an object is rotated clockwise or counterclockwise around a fixed point.

Example:

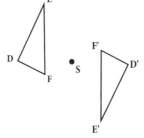

ΔDEF has been turned 180° clockwise about S. ΔD'E'F' is the image after the turn has occurred.

U

Unbiased

Not influenced or prejudiced by something external.

Example: A survey was given to students to see which field trip they were most interested in. A list of 4 choices was given and the students recorded their choice on a paper and handed their choices in without names recorded.

This is an example of an unbiased survey because students were not influenced by their classmates' choices, and the fact that they could vote anonymously allowed them to be more truthful in their selection.

Unit rate

A rate in which the second term (the denominator) is 1 unit.

Example: 22 students per teacher is a unit rate because it is the amount of students for one teacher.

Unit price
The price of one item; found by taking the total cost divided by the quantity of items.

    Example: 4 books cost $20.00.
               20 ÷ 4 = 5
               $5.00/book is the unit price.

V

Variable
A letter that represents an unknown quantity; the quantity can vary or change.

    Example: "*x*" represents the number of red cars in the parking lot.
               "*y*" represents a number.
               "*t*" represents the number of triangles.
               "*x*", "*y*", and "*t*" are examples of variables.

Verify
To substitute the value of the variable in the original equation with the solution and use order of operations to see if a true statement is reached.

    Example: 5*y*   =   35
               5(7)   =   35
               35   =   35 √

    This verifies that *y* = 7 is the solution to the equation 5*y* = 35.

Vertex
The point of intersection of two line segments or two faces.

    Example:

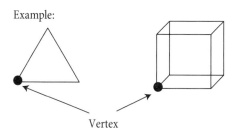

                        Vertex

Vertical

A line or object that is perpendicular to the horizon; travelling up and down.

Example:

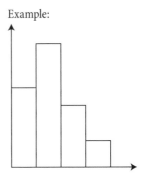

The bars in this graph are *vertical*.

Vertices

The points of intersections of two line segments or two faces; the plural of vertex.

Example:

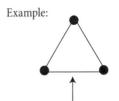

A triangle has three vertices.

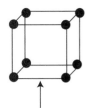

A cube has eight vertices.

Volume

A three dimensional measurement showing the amount of space an object occupies.

Volume = area of the base × the height of the object

Example:

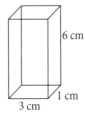

$V = (3 \times 1) \times 6$
$V = 3 \times 6$
$V = 18 \text{ cm}^3$

This volume of this object is 18 cm³.

W

Whole number
Positive counting numbers and the number zero; starting with zero and increasing by increments of one.

Example: W = {0, 1, 2, 3, 4 ...}

Width
The vertical distance from one point to another.

Example:

X

x-axis
The horizontal line in the coordinate plane.

Example:

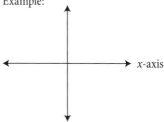

x-coordinate
The first number in an ordered pair; describes the distance along the x-axis from the origin.

Example: (3, -4)   The *x*-coordinate is +3; the point is three units right of the origin.

(-2, 5)   The *x*-coordinate is -2; the point is two units left of the origin.

Y

y-axis
The vertical line in the coordinate plane.

Example: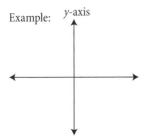

y-coordinate
The second number in an ordered pair; describes the distance along the y-axis from the origin.

Example: (3, -4)   The y-coordinate is -4; the point is four units down from the origin.
(-2, 5)   The y-coordinate is +5; the point is five units up from the origin.

Z

Zero
Having no value; the number from which all numbers are compared to as being either positive or negative.

Example: (+5) − (+5) = 0
If you start with five positives and you take away five positives, you have nothing left.

Numbers to the left   Numbers to the right
of zero are negative.   of zero are positive.

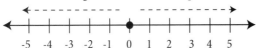

Zero principle
An equal number of positives and negatives combine to become zero.

Example:

Two positives and two negatives equal zero.

SURVIVAL GUIDE

Section I Boot Camp

Section II Reference

Formulas

Estimation

Sums and Differences

Example: Estimate the sum of 312.75 and 62.3.

    Step One: Identify the biggest number and its greatest place value.
                The biggest number is 312.87 and its greatest place value is the hundreds.

    Step Two: Round each number to the greatest place value of the biggest number.
                Round each number to the nearest hundred.

                312.75 ——➤ 300   62.3 ——➤ 100

    Step Three: Add/subtract the rounded numbers to get a final estimate.
                300 + 100 = 400   400 is an estimate.

Products

Example: Estimate the product of 68.9 and 8.91.

    Step One: Identify the greatest place value of each number.
                The greatest place value of 68.9 is the tens.
                The greatest place value of 8.91 is the ones.

    Step Two: Round each number to its greatest place value.
                68.9 ——➤ 70   8.91 ——➤ 9

    Step Three: Multiply the rounded numbers to get a final estimate.
                70 × 9 = 630   630 is an estimate.

note

For numbers less than 1, round to 0.5 or 1, whichever is closest.

Quotients

Example: Estimate the quotient of 17.5 ÷ 4.8.

    Step One: Round the dividend to its greatest place value.
                The greatest place value of 17.5 is the tens.17.5 ——➤ 20

    Step Two: Round the divisor to the closest factor of the rounded
                value in Step 1.
                Round the divisor (4.8) to be the closest factor of 20.
                4.8 ——➤ 5

    Step Three: Divide the rounded numbers to get a final estimate.
                20 ÷ 5 = 4   4 is an estimate.

note

For numbers less than 1, round to 0.5 or 1, whichever is closest.

Decimals

Sums and Differences

Example: Subtract 62.628 from 4 562.3.

    Step One: Line up the decimals and add zeros to make each number to the same place.

                   4562.**3**00
                −   62.628

Step Two: Add/subtract each digit separately from right to left as you would with whole numbers.

$$4^15^11\ {}^129$$
$$\cancel{4}\cancel{5}\cancel{6}\cancel{2}.\cancel{3}\cancel{0}\cancel{0}$$
$$-\qquad 6\ 2\ .\ 6\ 2\ 8$$
$$\overline{4\ 4\ 9\ 9\quad 6\ 7\ 2}$$

Step Three: Place the decimal point in the answer in line with those above.

$$4562.3$$
$$-\quad 62.628$$
$$\overline{4499{\small \bullet}672}$$

Products

Example: 512.36×2.31

Step One: To multiply decimals ignore the decimal and multiply digit by digit.

$$\begin{array}{r} 51236 \\ \times\quad 231 \\ \hline \mathbf{51236} \\ \mathbf{1537080} \\ \mathbf{10247200} \\ \hline \mathbf{11835516} \end{array}$$

Step Two: Find the total number of digits after the decimal in all factors. Move the decimal in your final answer left that number of times.
The first factor has 2 digits after the decimal and the second factor also has 2 digits after the decimal place. Move the decimal in the final answer left 4 (2 + 2 = 4) times.

$$1183.5516$$

Quotients

Example: Divide 59.2 by 0.16

Step One: Eliminate the decimal in the divisor by moving the decimal right to make it a whole number. Move the decimal in the dividend right the same number of times.
Move the decimal in the divisor right twice to make it a whole and repeat to the dividend.

$$59.2 \div 0.16 \qquad\qquad 59.20 \div 16$$

Step Two: Place the divisor outside the long division symbol and the dividend under it and divide as you would with whole numbers, adding a decimal point and zeros when necessary, to reach a remainder of zero or a pattern, in the case of a repeating decimal.

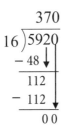

Order of Operations

Anytime a mathematical expression has more than two operations you must perform the operations in a specific order. You can remember the order of operations by using the acronym BEDMAS.

B	Brackets	
E	Exponents	
D	Division	} From left to right in the order that they appear.
M	Multiplication	
A	Addition	} From left to right in the order that they appear.
S	Subtraction	

Example: $4 \times 8 - 6 \div 2 \times 5$

Steps	Operation
$\mathbf{4 \times 8} - 6 \div 2 \times 5$	**M**ultiplication (because it came first left to right)
$32 - \mathbf{6 \div 2} \times 5$	**D**ivision (because it came first left to right)
$32 - \mathbf{3 \times 5}$	**M**ultiplication
$32 - 15$	**S**ubtraction
17	

Example: $3^2 - (7 - 3) + 4$

Steps	Operation
$3^2 - \mathbf{(7 - 3)} + 4$	**B**rackets
$\mathbf{3^2} - 4 + 4$	**E**xponents
$\mathbf{9 - 4} + 4$	**S**ubtraction
$\mathbf{5 + 4}$	**A**ddition
9	

Fractions

Improper Fractions ⟶ Mixed Numbers

Example: Write $\dfrac{9}{4}$ as a mixed number.

Step One: Using long division, divide the numerator by the denominator.

$$4\overline{)9} \quad \begin{array}{r} 2 \\ \underline{8} \\ 1 \end{array}$$

Step Two: Write as a mixed number using the following pattern.

Quotient (2)   =   Whole number part
Remainder (1)   =   Numerator of fraction
Divisor (4)   =   Denominator of fraction

$$\frac{9}{4} = 2\frac{1}{4}$$

Mixed Numbers ⟶ Improper Fractions

Example: Write $3\dfrac{2}{7}$ as an improper fraction.

Step One: Multiply the whole number by the denominator of the fraction.
$(3 \times 7) = 21$

Step Two: Add the product in Step one to the numerator of the fraction.
$21 + 2 = 23$

Step Three: The result from Step two becomes the numerator of the improper fraction and the denominator stays the same as it was in the mixed number.

$$3\frac{2}{7} = \frac{23}{7}$$

Fractions ⟶ Decimals

Example: Write $\dfrac{4}{5}$ in decimal form.

Step One: Convert any mixed numbers to improper fractions.
Doesn't apply in this example.

Step Two: Divide the numerator by the denominator.

$$5\overline{)4.0} \quad \begin{array}{r} 0.8 \\ \underline{-4\,0} \\ 0 \end{array}$$

0.8 ⟶ **Terminating decimal**

0 ⟶ Zero remainder

Example: Write $2\frac{3}{11}$ in decimal form.

Step One: Convert any mixed numbers to improper fractions.

$$2\frac{3}{11} = \frac{25}{11}$$

Step Two: Divide the numerator by the denominator.

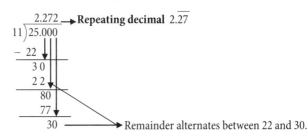

Repeating decimal $2.\overline{27}$

Remainder alternates between 22 and 30.

Decimals ⟶ Fractions

Example: Write 0.25 as a fraction in lowest terms.

Step One: Count the number of digits after the decimal.
Number of digits = Number of zeros following the one in the denominator.
0.25 has two digits after the decimal point, so the denominator will be 1 followed by two zeros (i.e. 0.25 is 25 hundredths).
Denominator = 100

Step Two: All of the digits after the decimal place = numerator. All of the digits before the decimal place = whole number and the fraction becomes a mixed number.
The numerator = all the digits after the decimal.
Numerator = 25

Step Three: Write the numerator and denominator together as a fraction and then reduce to lowest terms, if possible.

$$0.25 = \frac{25}{100}$$

$$0.25 = \frac{25 \div 25}{100 \div 25}$$

$$0.25 = \frac{1}{4}$$

Simplifying Fractions

Example: Write $\frac{9}{36}$ in lowest terms.

Step One: List the positive factors of both the numerator and denominator to determine the GCF.
factors of 9:   1, 3, 9
factors of 36:   1, 2, 3, 4, 6, 9, 12, 18, 36
GCF (9, 36) = 9

Step Two: Divide both the numerator and the denominator by the GCF.

$$\frac{9 \div 4}{36 \div 4} = \frac{1}{4}$$

$$\frac{9}{36} = \frac{1}{4} \text{ in lowest terms.}$$

Adding Fractions

Example: $\dfrac{1}{4} + \dfrac{2}{5}$

Step One: Write any mixed numbers as improper fractions.
Doesn't apply in this example.

Step Two: Change each fraction to an equivalent fraction with the LCM of the denominators as the "new" denominator.
LCM (4, 5) = 20

$$\left(\frac{1 \times 5}{4 \times 5} = \frac{5}{20} \right) \qquad \left(\frac{2 \times 4}{5 \times 4} = \frac{8}{20} \right)$$

Step Three: Add the numerators and place the sum over the common denominator.

$$\frac{5}{20} + \frac{8}{20} = \frac{13}{20}$$

Step Four: Write the fraction in lowest terms if possible.

$$\frac{1}{4} + \frac{2}{5} = \frac{13}{20}$$

Subtracting Fractions

Example: $1\dfrac{1}{9} - \dfrac{2}{5}$

Step One: Write any mixed numbers as improper fractions.
$$\frac{10}{9} - \frac{2}{5}$$

Step Two: Change each fraction to an equivalent fraction with the LCM of the denominators as the "new" denominator.

$$\left(\frac{10 \times 5}{9 \times 5} = \frac{50}{45} \right) \qquad \left(\frac{2 \times 9}{5 \times 9} = \frac{18}{45} \right)$$

Step Three: Subtract the numerators and place the difference over the common denominator.

$$\frac{50}{45} - \frac{18}{45} = \frac{32}{45}$$

Step Four: Write the fraction in lowest terms if possible.

$$1\frac{1}{9} - \frac{2}{5} = \frac{32}{45}$$

Multiplying Fractions

Example: $2\frac{1}{2} \times \frac{1}{5}$

Step One: Write any mixed numbers as improper fractions.

$$\frac{5}{2} \times \frac{1}{5}$$

Step Two: Multiply the numerators together and multiply the denominators together and place together as one fraction.

$$\frac{5}{10}$$

Step Three: Write the fraction in lowest terms if possible.

$$\frac{5 \div 5}{10 \div 5} = \frac{1}{2}$$

$$2\frac{1}{2} \times \frac{1}{5} = \frac{1}{2}$$

Dividing Fractions

Example: $1\frac{2}{3} \div \frac{2}{5}$

Step One: Write any mixed numbers as improper fractions.

$$\frac{5}{3} \div \frac{2}{5}$$

Step Two: Multiply the first fraction by the reciprocal of the second fraction.

$$\frac{5}{3} \times \frac{5}{2}$$

$$\frac{25}{6}$$

note

Reciprocal means to interchange the numerator and denominator.

Step Three: Write the fraction in lowest terms if possible.

$$\frac{25}{6} = 4\frac{1}{6}$$

$$1\frac{2}{3} \div \frac{2}{5} = 4\frac{1}{6}$$

Integers

Sums

Two positive integers
- The sign will be + and the numeric value will be the sum of the two numbers.

Example: (+9) + (+5)

(+9) + (+5) =   +   The sign is + since both numbers are positive.
(+9) + (+5) =   +14   The numeric value is 14 since 9 + 5 = 14.

Two negative integers
- The sign will be – and the numeric value will be the sum of the two numbers.

Example: (-3) + (-8)

(-3) + (-8) =   –   The sign is – since both numbers are negative.
(-3) + (-8) =   -11   The numeric value is 11 since 3 + 8 = 11.

A positive and a negative integer
- The sign will be the sign of the bigger number and the numeric value will be the difference of the two numbers.

Example: (+4) + (-6)

(+4) + (-6) =   –   The sign is – since 6 > 4.
(+4) + (-6) =   -2   The numeric value is 2 since 6 – 4 = 2.

Differences

Change any subtraction sentences to addition sentences first and then follow the integer rules of addition.

Step One: Keep the minuend (first number) the same.
Step Two: Change the operation of subtraction to addition.
Step Three: Change the subtrahend (second number) to its opposite sign.
Step Four: Calculate the sum of the new addition sentence.

Example: (-4) – (+7)   (+3) – (-6)
             ↓   ↓   ↓   ↓
             (-4) + (-7)   (+3) + (+6)

Example: (+5) – (+3)

(+5) + (-3) Change to an addition sentence.
(+5) + (-3) = +?   The sign is + since 5 > 3.
(+5) + (-3) = +2   The numeric value is 2 since 5 – 3 = 2.

Products

For the product of two numbers, if the signs match the product will be positive. If the signs don't match the sign will be negative. The numeric value will be the product of the two numbers.

Example: (+9) × (+3)

(+9) × (+3) = +?   The sign is + since the signs match.
(+9) × (+3) = + 27   The numeric value is 27 since 9 × 3 = 27.

Quotients

For the quotient of two numbers, if the signs match the quotient will be positive. If the signs don't match the sign will be negative. The numeric value will be the quotient of the two numbers.

Example: $(-44) \div (+2)$

$(-44) \div (+2) =$ $-$ The sign is $-$ since the signs don't match.
$(-44) \div (+2) =$ -22 The numeric value is 22 since $44 \div 2 = 22$.

Percents

Fractions ⟶ Percents

Example: Write $\frac{5}{8}$ as a percent.

Step One: Set up a proportion using the fraction as the first ratio and $\frac{x}{100}$ as the second ratio.

(The goal is to find the value of x, which gives the percent.)
$$\frac{5}{8} = \frac{x}{100}$$

Step Two: Multiply the numerator of the first ratio with the denominator of the second ratio and divide the result by the denominator of the first ratio. (Cross Multiply, and Divide!)

$\frac{5}{8} \searrow \frac{x}{100}$ Cross multiply, and divide.
$5 \times 100 = 500$
$500 \div 8 = 62.5$

Step Three: The value of x is the original ratio as a percent.
$$\frac{5}{8} = 62.5\%$$

Percents ⟶ Fractions

Example: Write 60% as a fraction in lowest terms.

Step One: Write the percent as a ratio with the second term of 100.
$$60\% = \frac{60}{100}$$

Step Two: Reduce the fraction by dividing numerator and denominator by GCF.
$$\frac{60 \div 20}{100 \div 20} = \frac{3}{5}$$
$$60\% = \frac{3}{5}$$

Percents ⟶ Decimals

Example: Write 35% as a decimal.

Step One: Write the percent as a fraction with a denominator of 100.

$$35\% = \frac{35}{100}$$

Step Two: Divide the numerator by 100, or move the decimal two places to the left.

$$35 \div 100 = 0.35 \qquad \text{or} \qquad 3\,5 = 0.35$$

Step Three: The result is the percent as a decimal.

35% as a decimal is 0.35.

Percent of a Number

Example: Find 30% of 56.

Step One: Change the percent to a decimal.
$$30\% = 0.30$$

Step Two: Multiply the decimal by the number.
$$0.30 \times 56 = 16.8$$

Estimating Percents

To help estimating, it is useful to be familiar with some common percentages.

10%	To find 10% of a number, move the decimal one place to the left.
25%	To find 25% (one-quarter) of a number, divide the number by 4.
50%	To find 50% (one-half) of a number, divide the number by 2.

Use the common percentages along with rounding skills to estimate percents.

Example: Estimate 11% of $28.

11% is close to 10%.

To estimate 11% of 28, find 10% of 28.

2 8

11% of $28 is about $2.80.

Example: Estimate 5% of 1167.

5% is half of 10%. Find 10% and then divide by 2 to get 5%.

10% of 1167 is 116.7.

Round 116.7 to the nearest number easily divisible by 2 (120).

$$120 \div 2 = 60$$

5% of 1167 is about 60.

Evaluating Algebraic Expressions

One Variable

Example: Evaluate $x + 5$, for $x = -8$.

   Step One: Start with the original expression.
                $x + 5$

   Step Two: Substitute (replace) each variable with its value. Use brackets to show your substitution.
                $(-8) + 5$

   Step Three: Use order of operations to evaluate the mathematical expression.
                -3

Two Variables

Example: Evaluate $2b + 3d$ if $b = 3$ and $d = -2$.

   Step One: Start with the original expression.
                $2b + 3d$

   Step Two: Substitute (replace) each variable with its value. Use brackets to show your substitution.
                $2(3) + 3(-2)$

   Step Three: Use order of operations to evaluate the mathematical expression.
                $6 + (-6)$
                0

Solving Equations Algebraically

One-step

Example: $y - 5 = 7$

   Step One: Identify the operation.
                $y - \mathbf{5} \quad = 7$ O: -5 Five was subtracted from the variable.

   Step Two: Identify and perform the inverse operation to **both** sides of the equation.
                $y - \cancel{5} \quad = 7$ I: $+5$ Adding five is the opposite.
                $\quad \cancel{+5} \quad +5$

   Step Three: Solve the equation and state the final answer.
                $y = 12$

   Step Four: Check the solution in the original equation.
                $y - 5 = 7$
                $(12) - 5 = 7$
                $\quad 7 = 7 \surd$

Two-step

Example: $\dfrac{x}{3} + 4 = -8$

    Step One: Identify the operation farthest away from the variable.

        $\dfrac{x}{3} + \mathbf{4} = -8$ O: +4

    Step Two: Identify and perform the inverse operation to both sides of the equation.

        $\dfrac{x}{3} + 4 = -8$ I: -4

        $\phantom{\dfrac{x}{3}}\mathbf{-4\ \ -4}$

        $\dfrac{x}{3} = -12$

    Step Three: Identify the operation.

        $\dfrac{x}{3} = -12$ O: $\div\,3$

    Step Four: Identify and perform the inverse operation to both sides of the equation.

        $\mathbf{3(\dfrac{x}{3}) = 3(-12)}$ I: $\times 3$

    Step Five: Solve the equation.

        $x = -36$

    Step Six: Check the solution in the original equation.

        $\dfrac{x}{3} + 4 = -8$

        $\dfrac{(-36)}{3} + 4 = -8$

        $-12 + 4 = -8$

        $-8 = -8\ \sqrt{}$

Variables on Both Sides

Example: $8x - 10 = -2x - 20$

    Step One: To keep the variable positive, eliminate the least/smallest (i.e. "coldest") variable.

        $8x - 10 = \mathbf{-2x} - 20$ O: $-2x$

        $\mathbf{+2x}\mathbf{+2x}$ I: $+2x$

    Step Two: Isolate the variable using operations and inverse operations farthest from the variable.

        $10x - \mathbf{10} = -20$ O: -10

        $\mathbf{+10\ \ +10}$ I: $+\,10$

        $\dfrac{\mathbf{10x}}{\mathbf{10}} = \dfrac{\mathbf{-10}}{\mathbf{10}}$ O: $\times 10$

                I: $\div 10$

    Step Three: State the final answer.

        $x = -1$

    Step Four: Check the solution in the original equation.

        $8x - 10 = -2x - 20$

        $8(-1) - 10 = -2(-1) - 20$

        $-8 - 10 = 2 - 20$

        $-8 + (-10) = 2 + (-20)$

        $-18 = -18\ \sqrt{}$

Equations with Brackets

Example: $2(x - 3) - 5 = 13 - 4x$

Step One: Use the distributive property to eliminate the brackets and simplify.

$2(x - 3)$ becomes $2x - 6$
$2x - 6 - 5 = 13 - 4x$
$2x - 11 = 13 - 4x$

Step Two: Get the variable on one side of the equation.

$$2x - 11 = 13 - 4x$$
$$2x - 11 = 13 - 4x \qquad O: -4x$$
$$+4x \qquad\qquad +4x \qquad I: +4x$$

Step Three: Isolate the variable using operations and inverse operations farthest from the variable.

$$6x - 11 = 13 \qquad\qquad O: -11$$
$$+11 \quad +11 \qquad\qquad I: + 11$$
$$\frac{6x}{6} = \frac{24}{6} \qquad\qquad O: \times 6$$
$$\qquad\qquad\qquad I: \div 6$$

Step Four: State and check the final answer.

$$x = 4$$
$$2(x - 3) - 5 = 13 - 4x$$
$$2(4 - 3) - 5 = 13 - 4(4)$$
$$2(1) - 5 = 13 - 16$$
$$2 - 5 = 13 - 16$$
$$2 + (-5) = 13 + (-16)$$
$$-3 = -3 \ \sqrt{}$$

Equations with Fractions

Example: $\dfrac{x + 1}{3} = \dfrac{x - 7}{7}$

Step One: Identify the LCM of the denominators and multiply both sides by it.

$$21\left(\frac{x + 1}{3}\right) = 21\left(\frac{x - 7}{7}\right) \qquad \text{LCM } (3, 7): 21$$
$$7(x + 1) = 3(x - 7)$$

note

$21 \div 3 = 7$ and
$21 \div 7 = 3$

Step Two: Use the distributive property to eliminate the brackets and simplify.

$$7(x + 1) = 3(x - 7)$$
$$7x + 7 = 3x - 21$$

Step Three: Get the variable on one side of the equation.

$$7x + 7 = 3x - 21 \qquad O: +3x$$
$$-3x \qquad -3x \qquad\qquad I: -3x$$

Step Four: Isolate the variable using operations and inverse operations farthest from the variable.

$$4x + 7 = -21$$
$$-7 \quad -7 \qquad \text{O: } +7$$
$$\qquad\qquad\qquad \text{I: } -7$$
$$\frac{4x}{4} = \frac{-28}{4} \qquad \text{O: } \times 4$$
$$\qquad\qquad\qquad \text{I: } \div 4$$

Step Five: State and check your final answer.

$$x = -7$$
$$\frac{x+1}{3} = \frac{x-7}{7}$$
$$\frac{(-7)+1}{3} = \frac{(-7)-7}{7}$$
$$\frac{-6}{3} = \frac{-14}{7}$$
$$-2 = -2 \ \checkmark$$

Inequalities

Solving

Solve inequalities using the same rules used for solving equations.

If both sides of the inequality are multiplied or divided by a negative number, the inequality sign must be reversed.

Example: $-3w + 4 < 16$, $w \in I$.

$$-3w + 4 < 16 \qquad \text{O: } + 4$$
$$-4 \quad -4 \qquad \text{I: } - 4$$
$$\frac{-3w}{-3} < \frac{12}{-3} \qquad \text{O: } \times(-3)$$
$$\qquad\qquad \text{I: } \div (-3)$$
$$w > -4 \qquad \text{Both sides were divided by -3 so the inequality sign was reversed.}$$
$$w = \{-3, -2, -1, 0 \ldots\}$$

Check: $w > -4$ means any integer greater than -4 (ie: $w = -3, -2, -1, 0 \ldots$). To check the solution, use any point greater than -4 in the original inequality.

$$-3w + 4 < 16$$
$$-3(-3) + 4 < 16$$
$$9 + 4 < 16$$
$$13 < 16 \ \checkmark$$

Graphing the Solution

If the solution set is from the set of integers, dots on the number line are used to show which positive or negative whole numbers are included.

If the solution set includes real numbers, a solid line is used to show the solution includes positive and negative whole numbers and everything in-between (decimals and fractions).

An open dot is used to show the starting number is not part of the solution.

A closed dot is used to show the starting number is part of the solution.

Example: $x > -3; x \in \Re$

A solid line is used because the solution contains real numbers. A solid line starting at -3, but not including -3 (hence the open dot) is drawn to the right, indicating the numbers greater than -3.

Example: $x \leq 4; x \in I$

Individual dots are used because the solution is from the set of integers. The dots start at 4, including 4 (hence the closed dot) and continue to the left, indicating the numbers less than 4.

Conversions

Linear Measurements

Example: Convert 4.5 m to mm.

Step One: Locate the given amount as the start point on the linear scale.

Step Two: Locate the needed amount as the end point on the linear scale.

Step Three: Count the number of jumps and note the direction needed to move from start to end.

Kilo	Hecto	Deca	Unit (metres) START	Deci	Centi	Milli END

3 places right

Step Four: Move the decimal point in the given amount the same number of jumps in the same direction. Place zeros in any empty bumps.

4. 5 0 0

3 places right

4.5 m = 4 500 mm

Example: Convert 400 000 mL to kL.

Step One: Locate the given amount as the start point on the linear scale.

Step Two: Locate the needed amount as the end point on the linear scale.

Step Three: Count the number of jumps and note the direction needed to move from start to end.

Kilo	Hecto	Deca	Unit	Deci	Centi	Milli
END			(litres)			**START**

6 places left

Step Four: Move the decimal in the given amount in that direction that number of spaces.
            Place zeros in any empty bumps.

4 0 0 0 0 0

6 places left

400 000 mL = 0.4 kL

Area

Example: Convert 4.5 cm² to mm².

Step One: Locate the given amount as the start point on the linear scale.

Step Two: Locate the needed amount as the end point on the linear scale.

Step Three: Count the number of jumps and note the direction needed to move from start to end.

Kilo	Hecto	Deca	Unit	Deci	Centi	Milli
			(square metres)			
					START	**END**

1 place right

Step Four: Move the decimal point in the given amount DOUBLE the number of jumps in the same direction. Place zeros in any empty bumps.

4. 5 0

$1 \times 2 = 2$ places right

$4.5 \text{ cm}^2 = 4\ 50 \text{ mm}^2$

Volume

Example: Convert 7 500 cL^3 to L^3.

    Step One: Locate the given amount as the start point on the linear scale.

    Step Two: Locate the needed amount as the end point on the linear scale.

    Step Three: Count the number of jumps and note the direction needed to move from start to end.

Kilo	Hecto	Deca	Unit (cubic litres) END	Deci	Centi START	Milli

2 places left

    Step Four: Move the decimal point in the given amount TRIPLE the number of jumps in the same direction. Place zeros in any empty bumps.

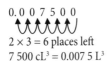

$2 \times 3 = 6$ places left

7 500 cL^3 = 0.007 5 L^3

Surface Area

Draw the net of the object and find the area of each face.

Prism

Example: Calculate the surface area.

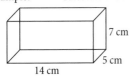

    Step One: Draw and label the net of the three-dimensional object.

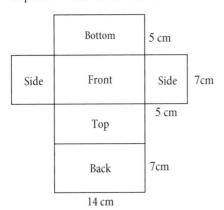

Step Two: Find the area of each of face in the net.

Top/Bottom (2)	Front/Back (2)	Sides (2)
$A = l \times w$	$A = l \times w$	$A = l \times w$
$A = 14 \times 5$	$A = 14 \times 7$	$A = 5 \times 7$
$A = 70$	$A = 98$	$A = 35$
$2 \times 70 = 140$	$2 \times 98 = 196$	$2 \times 35 = 70$

Step Three: Find the sum of all the areas and state final answer with the appropriate units.

$SA = 140 + 196 + 70$

$SA = 406 \text{ cm}^2$

Cylinder

Example: Calculate the surface area.

Step One: Draw and label the net of the three-dimensional object.

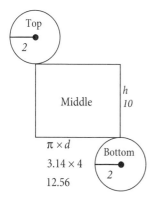

Step Two: Find the area of each of face in the net.

Top/Bottom (2)	Middle
$A = \pi r^2$	$A = lw$
$A = 3.14 \times 2^2$	$A = 12.56 \times 10$
$A = 3.14 \times 4$	$A = 125.6$
$A = 12.56$	
$2 \times 12.56 = 25.12$	

Step Three: Find the sum of all the areas and state final answer with the appropriate units.

$SA = 25.12 + 125.6$

$SA = 150.72 \text{ cm}^2$

Cone

Example: Calculate the surface area.

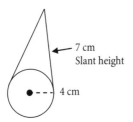

7 cm
Slant height

4 cm

Step One: Draw and label the net of the three-dimensional object.

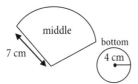

middle

bottom

7 cm

4 cm

Step Two: Find the area of each face in the net.

Bottom
$A = \pi r^2$
$A = (3.14) \times (4)^2$
$A = 50.24$

Middle
$A = \pi rs$
$A = (3.14) \times (4) \times (7)$
$A = 87.92$

Step Three: Find the sum of all the areas and state the final answer with the appropriate units.

$SA = 50.24 + 87.92$
$SA = 138.16 \text{ cm}^2$

Volume

Find the area of the base and multiply it by the height of the object.

If the three dimensional object comes to a point (eg: cone or pyramid), divide the volume of the object by three.

If one of the faces of a prism is a triangle, the triangle must be the base.

Cylinder

Example: Calculate the volume.

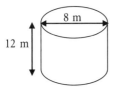

8 m

12 m

Step One: Identify the shape of the base and calculate its area.

$A = \pi \times r^2$

$A = 3.14 \times (4)^2$

$A = 3.14 \times 16$

$A = 50.24 \text{ m}^2$

Step Two: Multiply the height of the object by the area of the base.

$50.24 \times 12 = 602.88$

Step Three: State final answer with the appropriate units.

Volume $= 602.88 \text{ m}^3$

Pyramid

Example: Calculate the volume.

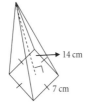

Step One: Identify the shape of the base and calculate its area.

$A = (s)^2$

$A = (7)^2$

$A = 49$

Step Two: Multiply the height of the object by the area of the base.

$49 \times 14 = 686$

$686 \div 3 = 228.7$ Since the object comes to a point, divide the volume by three.

Step Three: State final answer with the appropriate units.

Volume $= 228.7 \text{ cm}^3$

Scientific Notation

A number written in scientific notation is a decimal (with one number in front of the decimal point) multiplied by a power of ten.

The power of ten will have a positive exponent for numbers >1.

The power of ten will have a negative exponent for numbers <1.

Large numbers ⟶ Scientific notation

Example: Write 432 000 000 in scientific notation.

Step One: Identify where the decimal point is as the start point.

Step Two: Identify where the decimal point needs to be (so as to have one non-zero digit in front) as the end point.

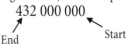

End   Start

Step Three: Count left the number of spaces needed to move from the start point to the end point. This number represents the positive exponent in the power of ten.

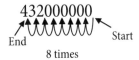

432000000

End   Start

8 times

Step Four: Write the number in scientific notation; drop any unnecessary zeros.

4.32×10^8

Small numbers ⟶ Scientific notation

Example: Convert 0.000 000 125 into scientific notation.

Step One: Identify where the decimal point is as the start point.

Step Two: Identify where the decimal point needs to be (so as to have one non-zero digit in front) as the end point.

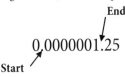

End

0.0000001.25

Start

Step Three: Count right the number of spaces needed to move from the start point to the end point. This number represents the negative exponent in the power of ten.

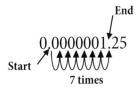

End

0.0000001.25

Start

7 times

Step Four: Write the number in scientific notation; drop any unnecessary zeros.

1.25×10^{-7}

Monomials

Multiplying

Multiply coefficients together.

Multiply variables with the same base together by adding the exponents.

Example: $(4x)(-3x)$

$-12x^2$ Because $4 \times -3 = -12$ and $x^{1+1} = x^2$.

Example: $(4x^2y^3)(5xy^2)$

$20x^3y^5$ Because $4 \times 5 = 20$, $x^{2+1} = x^3$ and $y^{3+2} = y^5$.

Dividing

Divide coefficients together.

Divide variables with the same base together by subtracting the
exponents.

Example: $\dfrac{-24\,x^2\,y^6}{3x^2\,y^4}$

note

$x^0 = 1$ so we
don't need to
include it.

-8y^2 Because -24 ÷ 3 = -8 and $x^{2-2} = x^0$ and $y^{6-4} = y^2$.

Example: $\dfrac{48\,x^2\,y^8}{36\,x^5\,y^4}$

note

$x^{-3} = \dfrac{1}{x^3}$

$\dfrac{4\,y^4}{3x^3}$ Because $\dfrac{48 \div 12}{36 \div 12} = \dfrac{4}{3}$ and $x^{2-5} = x^{-3}$ and $y^{8-4} = y^4$.

Binomial Products

First terms   (Multiply the first terms of each binomial together.)

Outside terms   (Multiply the outside terms of each binomial together.)

Inside terms   (Multiply the inside terms of each binomial together.)

Last terms   (Multiply the last terms of each binomial together.)

Example: $(x + 2)(x + 2)$

First terms $(x)(x) = x^2$
Outside terms $(2)(x) = 2x$
Inside terms $(2)(x) = 2x$
Last terms $(2)(2) = 4$

F   O   I   L
$x^2 + 2x + 2x + 4$
$x^2 + 4x + 4$ Collect like terms.

Polynomials

Adding

Combine like terms and add the coefficients; the variable part of the term stays the same.

Example: $(x^2 + 4x - 5) + (2x^2 - 5x + 1)$

Step One: Remove the brackets.
           $x^2 + 4x - 5 + 2x^2 - 5x + 1$

Step Two: Collect like terms and add.
           $x^2 + 2x^2 + 4x - 5x - 5 + 1$
           $3x^2 - x - 4$

Subtracting

Change to an addition sentence by adding the additive inverse of the second polynomial.

Combine like terms and add the coefficients; the variable part of the term stays the same.

Example: $(x^2 + 4x - 5) - (3x^2 - 4x + 4)$

Step One: Keep the first polynomial the same, change the operation to addition and the second polynomial to its additive inverse.
$(x^2 + 4x - 5) + (-3x^2 + 4x - 4)$

Step Two: Remove the brackets.
$x^2 + 4x - 5 + -3x^2 + 4x - 4$

Step Three: Collect like terms and add.
$x^2 + -3x^2 + 4x + 4x - 5 - 4$
$-2x^2 + 8x - 9$

Multiplying

Example: $3x(x - 3) - 4(x + 3)$

Step One: Use the distributive property to expand each expression.
$3x(x - 3) - 4(x + 3)$

$3x(x - 3) - 4(x + 3)$
$3x^2 - 9x - 4x - 12$

Step Two: Collect like terms (simplify).
$3x^2 - 13x - 12$

Dividing

Example: $\dfrac{-24ab^6 + 8a^2b^3 - 4ab}{4ab}$

Step One: Break up into separate fractions.
$\dfrac{-24ab^6}{4ab} + \dfrac{8a^2b^3}{4ab} - \dfrac{4ab}{4ab}$

Step Two: Simplify each fraction.
$-6b^5 + 2ab^2 - 1$

Factoring

Common Factors

Example: Factor $6m^2n + 9mn$.

Step One: Write each expression as a product of its prime factors and identify factors common to each expression.
$6m^2n = (2)\,(3)\,(m)\,(m)\,(n)$
$9mn = (3)\,(3)\,(m)\,(n)$

Step Two: Multiply the common factors together to calculate the GCF.
$3 \times m \times n = 3mn$ \qquad GCF $= 3mn$

Step Three: Write the product of the GCF and the unused factors from each monomial.
$3mn(2m + 3)$

Example: Factor $2x^3 + 8x^2 - 4x$.

  Step One: Write each expression as a product of its prime factors and identify factors
            common to each expression.
            $2x^3 = $ **(2)** **(x)** (x) (x)
            $8x^2 = $ **(2)** (2) (2) **(x)** (x)
            $-4x = $ **(2)** (-2) **(x)**

  Step Two: Multiply the common factors together to calculate the GCF.
            $2 \times x = 2x$ GCF $= 2x$

  Step Three: Write the product of the GCF and the unused factors from each monomial.
            $2x(x^2 + 4x - 2)$

Factoring Trinomials $(x^2 + bx + c)$
Example: Factor $x^2 + 7x + 10$.

  Step One: Find two numbers that multiply to the last number (c) and add to number in
            front of x (b).
            +5 and +2

  Step Two: Check.
            $5 \times 2 = 10\sqrt{}$ $5 + 2 = 7\sqrt{}$

  Step Three: Draw two pairs of brackets. In the first brackets place x and the first number
            and in the second brackets place x and the second number.
            $(x + 5) (x + 2)$

Example: Factor $x^2 + 4x - 21$.

  Step One: Find two numbers that multiply to the last number (c) and add to number in
            front of x (b).
            -3 and +7

  Step Two: Check.
            $(-3) \times (+7) = -21\sqrt{}$ $(-3) + (+7) = +4\sqrt{}$

  Step Three: Draw two pairs of brackets. In the first brackets place x and the first number
            and in the second brackets place x and the second number.
            $(x - 3) (x + 7)$

Trigonometry
Pythagorean Theorem
The length of the hypotenuse squared (c^2) equals the length of the horizontal leg squared
(a^2) added to the length of the vertical leg squared (b^2)

$a^2 + b^2 = c^2$

Example:

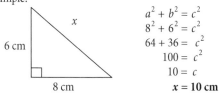

$$a^2 + b^2 = c^2$$
$$8^2 + 6^2 = c^2$$
$$64 + 36 = c^2$$
$$100 = c^2$$
$$10 = c$$
$$x = 10 \text{ cm}$$

Example:

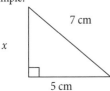

$$a^2 + b^2 = c^2$$
$$5^2 + b^2 = 7^2$$
$$25 + b^2 = 49$$
$$b^2 = 24$$
$$b = 4.9$$
$$x = \textbf{4.9 cm}$$

Trigonometric Ratios

SOH
$$\textbf{S}\text{ine} = \frac{\textbf{o}\text{pposite}}{\textbf{h}\text{ypotenuse}}$$

CAH
$$\textbf{C}\text{osine} = \frac{\textbf{a}\text{djacent}}{\textbf{h}\text{ypotenuse}}$$

TOA
$$\textbf{T}\text{angent} = \frac{\textbf{o}\text{pposite}}{\textbf{a}\text{djacent}}$$

Example:

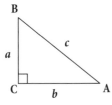

$$\text{Sin} \angle \textbf{A} = \frac{a}{c} \qquad \text{Cos} \angle \textbf{A} = \frac{b}{c} \qquad \text{Tan} \angle \textbf{A} = \frac{a}{b}$$

$$\text{Sin} \angle \textbf{B} = \frac{b}{c} \qquad \text{Cos} \angle \textbf{B} = \frac{a}{c} \qquad \text{Tan} \angle \textbf{B} = \frac{b}{a}$$

Finding a Missing Side

Example: Solve for "x".

Step One: Decide which of the three trig ratios you need to use and write down the formula.

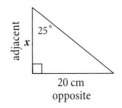

$$\text{Tangent } \theta = \frac{\text{opposite}}{\text{adjacent}}$$

Step Two: Substitute the given values.

$$\frac{Tan(25°)}{1} = \frac{20}{x}$$

Step Three: Solve for the missing value.

$$\frac{Tan(25°)}{1} = \frac{20}{x}$$

$$x = \textbf{42.9 cm}$$

$1 \times 20 = 20$

$20 \div \tan 25 = 42.9$

Finding a Missing Angle

Example: Solve for "x".

Step One: Decide which of the three trig ratios you need to use and write down the formula.

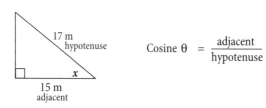

$$\text{Cosine } \theta = \frac{\text{adjacent}}{\text{hypotenuse}}$$

Step Two: Substitute the given values.

$$\frac{Cos(x)}{1} = \frac{15}{17}$$

Step Three: Solve for the missing value.

$$\frac{Cos(x)}{1} = \frac{15}{17}$$

$1 \times 15 = 15$

$15 \div 17 = 0.882\ 352\ 41$

$Cos^{-1}(0.882\ 352\ 41) = 28°$

$$x = \textbf{28°}$$

Formulas

Perimeter

Rectangle	$P = 2(l + w)$	l = length w = width
Square	$P = 4s$	s = side length
Regular polygon	$P = ns$	n = number of sides s = side length

Circumference

Circle	$C = \pi d$	π = 3.14 d = diameter
Circle	$C = 2\pi r$	π = 3.14 r = radius

Area

Rectangle	$A = lw$	l = length w = width
Square	$A = s^2$	s = side length
Parallelogram	$A = bh$	b = base h = height
Triangle	$A = \dfrac{bh}{2}$	b = base h = height
Trapezoid	$A = \dfrac{h(a + b)}{2}$	a, b = base h = height
Circle	$A = \pi r^2$	π = 3.14 r = radius

Surface Area

Cylinder	$SA = 2\pi r^2 + \pi dh$	π = 3.14 r = radius d = diameter h = height

Cone	$SA = \pi r^2 + \pi rs$	$\pi = 3.14$
		r = radius
		s = slant height

Cube	$SA = 6s^2$	s = side length

Rectangular prism	$SA = 2lw + 2wh + 2lh$	l = length
		w = width
		h = height

Volume

Rectangular prism	$V = lwh$	l = length
		w = width
		h = height

Prism	$V = Bh$	B = area of the base
		h = height

Cylinder	$V = \pi r^2 h$	$\pi = 3.14$
		r = radius
		h = height

Cone	$V = \dfrac{\pi r^2 h}{3}$	$\pi = 3.14$
		r = radius
		h = height

Pyramid	$V = \dfrac{Bh}{3}$	B = area of the base
		h = height

Temperature Conversions

Fahrenheit	$F = \dfrac{9}{5}C + 32$	C = temperature in Celsius

Celsius	$C = \dfrac{5}{9}(F - 32)$	F = temperature in Fahrenheit

Interest

Simple Interest	$I = PRT$	P = principle
		R = Interest rate as a decimal
		T = time in years

Symbols

+	plus or add	$\overline{AB}$	line segment AB
−	minus or subtract	$\overrightarrow{AB}$	ray AB
×	times or multiply	∠ABC	angle ABC
÷	divide	m∠ABC	measure angle ABC
=	equal	△ ABC	triangle ABC
≠	not equal to	∈	is an element of
>	greater than		
<	less than		
≥	greater than or equal to		
≤	less than or equal to		
≈	approximately equal to		
≅	congruent to		
~	similar to		
$	dollar sign		
¢	cent sign		
%	percent		
π	pi (approximately 3.14)		
°	degree		
°C	degree Celsius		
°F	degree Fahrenheit		
…	continues without end		
$1.\overline{3}$	repeating decimal 1.333…		
a^b	a to the exponent b		
$\sqrt{\ }$	square root		
:	is to; used in proportions		
2:5	ratio of 2 to 5		
+4	positive 4		
-4	negative 4		
P(E)	probability of event E		
$\overleftrightarrow{AB}$	line AB		

×	1	2	3	4	5	6	7	8	9	10	11	12	13	14	15	16	17	18	19	20
1	1	2	3	4	5	6	7	8	9	10	11	12	13	14	15	16	17	18	19	20
2	2	4	6	8	10	12	14	16	18	20	22	24	26	28	30	32	34	36	38	40
3	3	6	9	12	15	18	21	24	27	30	33	36	39	42	45	48	51	54	57	60
4	4	8	12	16	20	24	28	32	36	40	44	48	52	56	60	64	68	72	76	80
5	5	10	15	20	25	30	35	40	45	50	55	60	65	70	75	80	85	90	95	100
6	6	12	18	24	30	36	42	48	54	60	66	72	78	84	90	96	102	108	114	120
7	7	14	21	28	35	42	49	56	63	70	77	84	91	98	105	112	119	126	133	140
8	8	16	24	32	40	48	56	64	72	80	88	96	104	112	120	128	136	144	152	160
9	9	18	27	36	45	54	63	72	81	90	99	108	117	126	135	144	153	162	171	180
10	10	20	30	40	50	60	70	80	90	100	110	120	130	140	150	160	170	180	190	200
11	11	22	33	44	55	66	77	88	99	110	121	132	143	154	165	176	187	198	209	220
12	12	24	36	48	60	72	84	96	108	120	132	144	156	168	180	192	204	216	228	240
13	13	26	39	52	65	78	91	104	117	130	143	156	169	182	195	208	221	234	247	260
14	14	28	42	56	70	84	98	112	126	140	154	168	182	196	210	224	238	252	266	280
15	15	30	45	60	75	90	105	120	135	150	165	180	195	210	225	240	255	270	285	300
16	16	32	48	64	80	96	112	128	144	160	176	192	208	224	240	256	272	288	304	320
17	17	34	51	68	85	102	119	136	153	170	187	204	221	238	255	272	289	306	323	340
18	18	36	54	72	90	108	126	144	162	180	198	216	234	252	270	288	306	324	342	360
19	19	38	57	76	95	114	133	152	171	190	209	228	247	266	285	304	323	342	361	380
20	20	40	60	80	100	120	140	160	180	200	220	240	260	280	300	320	340	360	380	400